Instructors Manual
with Tests
and Transparency Masters

CRIMINALISTICS

An Introduction to Forensic Science

Seventh Edition

RICHARD SAFERSTEIN

Prentice
Hall

Upper Saddle River, New Jersey 07458

10 9 8 7 6 5 4 3 2 1

ISBN: 0-13-020532-X

CONTENTS

Preface   v

CHAPTER 1   Introduction   1

CHAPTER 2   The Crime Scene   4

CHAPTER 3   Physical Evidence   7

CHAPTER 4   Physical Properties: Glass and Soil   9

CHAPTER 5   Organic Analysis   14

CHAPTER 6   Inorganic Analysis   18

CHAPTER 7   The Microscope   21

CHAPTER 8   Hairs, Fibers, and Paint   24

CHAPTER 9   Drugs   27

CHAPTER 10   Forensic Toxicology   31

CHAPTER 11   Forensic Aspects of Arson and Explosion Investigations   36

CHAPTER 12   Forensic Serology   40

CHAPTER 13   DNA-A New Forensic Science Tool   45

CHAPTER 14   Fingerprints   49

CHAPTER 15   Firearms, Tool Marks, and Other Impressions   52

CHAPTER 16   Document and Voice Examination   55

CHAPTER 17   Forensic Science on the Internet   58

Answers to Chapter Review Questions   60

List of Transparency Masters   66

PREFACE

This guide has been prepared as a supplement to *Criminalistics: An Introduction to Forensic Science*, which has been written as a basic introductory text in criminalistics. It is designed for a one-semester course of about 13 to 15 weeks in duration. By covering about one chapter per week, an instructor should have little difficulty in completing all the topics contained within the text. The author fully realizes that because of the varied backgrounds and experience of the instructors teaching this course, there may be a desire on the part of some to deviate from the prescribed order of the text. Hence, once the fundamental chapters (1-7) of the text are covered, subsequent chapters may be taken in almost any order or may be omitted without hurting the continuity of the course.

I want to emphasize that it is not the purpose of the text or course to make forensic experts or scientists out of the students. Teaching the proper utilization of crime laboratory services to criminal justice students is sufficient justification in itself for a course of this nature. Optimum performance of duty by present and future members of the law enforcement community will depend, in large part, on their abilities to interact with pertinent members of the scientific community. I look upon this course as a golden opportunity to emphasize those facets of criminal investigation that pertain directly to forensic analysis.

Though some basic scientific principles and techniques are taught, their inclusion is primarily meant to demonstrate the workings and limitations of a crime laboratory, as well as the value of physical evidence. As an instructor of criminalistics for several years, I would caution anyone from venturing much beyond the instructional level I have sought to establish in this text. The tolerance of the average criminal justice student for subjects relating to the natural and physical sciences is extremely low. One must always be conscious of the likelihood that a student can be very quickly turned off by all the science and lose sight of the relevant objectives of an introductory criminalistics course.

Whenever possible, the instructor should be encouraged to supplement text material with audio-visual aids, as well as with personal experiences relating to the conduct of scientific police investigations. The case readings contained within the text will assist those who cannot claim actual field experience in this area. It is suggested that the case readings be discussed in conjunction with the following chapters:

1. Detection of Curare in the Jascalevich Murder Trial — Chapters 1 and 10
2. The Enrique Camarena Case: A Forensic Nightmare — Chapter 2
3. Fiber Evidence and the Wayne Williams Trial — Chapters 3 and 8
4. Outrage: The O.J. Simpson Verdict — Chapters 3 and 13
5. Microscopic Trace Evidence-The Overlooked Clue — Chapter 7

6. The "Bobby Joe" Long Serial Murder Case: A Study in Cooperation   Chapters 8 and 12

7. Attempted Assassination of Archbishop Makarios   Chapters 8 and 14

8. Teamwork in the Forensic Sciences   Chapters 15 or 16

Most chapters in the text have accompanying review questions to help the reader highlight the chapter's contents. Answers to the odd-numbered questions are provided in the appendix of the text. The instructor will find the answers to the even-numbered questions on the back pages of this manual.

Like all facets of modern-life, forensic science has been touched by the Internet. There are many interesting and relevant web sites dealing with subjects covered in this text. For this reason, this edition of "Criminalistics" contains a chapter introducing the reader to basic concepts of the Internet. The chapter also includes web sites that the author believes readers of this text will find interesting and educational and will integrate well with the contents of this book. Keep in mind that the Internet is in a constant state of flux, so that it's up to instructors to keep themselves apprised of changes and updating. Chapter 17 should give the reader a good start in this direction.

Transparency masters are provided to help you with the use of visual aids in the classroom. The masters contain the same figure numbers as used in the text. This will provide for easy location and reference.

For those planning to incorporate a laboratory session into the course, you will find within this guide some suggestions for laboratory experiments. Additionally, a companion text, "A Laboratory Manual for Criminalistics," by James, Meloan, and Saferstein (Prentice Hall, 1998) has been published to provide forensic experiments at an instructional level compatible with the student readers of this book. It is also the purpose of this guide to list learning objectives for each chapter, as well as questions that may be useful for examinations.

Good Luck!
R.S.

INTRODUCTION

LEARNING OBJECTIVES

1. Define forensic science or criminalistics.
2. Recall the major contributors to the development of forensic science.
3. Give examples of typical crime laboratories as they exist on the national, state, and local levels of government in the United States.
4. Describe the services of a typical comprehensive crime laboratory in the criminal justice system.
5. Explain the different approaches espoused by the Frye and Daubert decisions to the admissibility of scientific evidence in the courtroom.
6. Explain the role and responsibilities of the expert witness.
7. Review the proper collection and packaging of common types of physical evidence as described in Appendix I.
8. Introduce the student to other areas of forensic science that require expertise in a specialized area.

GENERAL COMMENTS

Students should become familiar with the organization and capabilities of your state and local forensic laboratories. Usually, this can be accomplished through brochures and pamphlets that are prepared by these facilities. The instructor may want to arrange a class tour of one of these laboratories, or perhaps engage the cooperation of a forensic laboratory in order to prepare a slide presentation showing pertinent sections of the installation.

Students should be referred to the Internet Web sites, "Carpenter's Forensic Science Resources" (http://www.public.usit.net/rscarp/forensic.htm) and "The Science of Crime" (http://whyfiles.news.wisc.edu/014/forensic/index.html). Each of these sites provides information regarding topics such as DNA, hairs, fibers, and questioned documents. These Web sites are an excellent place to start a research project in forensic science.

SUGGESTED EXAMINATION QUESTIONS

__c__ 1. One of the earliest crime laboratories was founded by:
   a. Albert Osborn
   b. Hans Gross
   c. Edmond Locard
   d. Leone Lattes
   e. Francis Galton

 b   2. The judicial case that set forth the guidelines for determining the admissibility of scientific examinations in the Federal courts is:
a. *Frye* v. *United States*
b. *Daubert* v. *Merrell Dow Pharmaceuticals*
c. *Coppolino* v. *State of Florida*
d. *Mapp* v. *United States*
e. *People* v. *Williams*

 d   3. The case of *Frye* v. *United States* deals with the legal issue of:
a. Admissibility of photographs in court
b. Search and seizure guidelines
c. Defining the term "expert witness"
d. General acceptance of scientific principles
e. Admissibility of fingerprint evidence

 d   4. The following service does not normally lie within the expertise of the forensic scientist:
a. Drug identification
b. Wood comparisons
c. Document examination
d. Polygraph examination
e. Latent fingerprint examination

 e   5. The effectiveness of an expert's testimony is almost always dependent on:
a. The experience of the expert
b. The ability of the expert to talk in clear, concise language
c. The educational background of the expert
d. The scientific validity of the tests used
e. All of the above

 b   6. The process by which the body temperature cools after death is known as:
a. Rigor mortis
b. Algor mortis
c. Livor mortis
d. Denaturation
e. Ambient degradation

__e__   7. Which of the following techniques can be used to estimate the time of death?
  a. Rigor mortis
  b. Eye fluid potassium levels
  c. Livor mortis
  d. Insect infestation
  e. All of the above

8. List the functions of a forensic scientist.

   Answer:
   a. Analyzes physical evidence
   b. Provides expert testimony
   c. Furnishes training in recognizing, collecting, and preserving physical evidence at crime scenes

9. Discuss the underlying reasons for the rapid growth of crime laboratories in the U.S. since the late 1960s.

   Answer:
   a. The increasing volume of physical evidence recovered from crime scenes as a result of rising crime rates
   b. The need to perform chemical analyses on drugs, coupled with a significant increase in illicit drug seizures
   c. Supreme Court decisions have enhanced the rights of the defendant. Decisions, such as those insuring a defendant's right to counsel and the right to remain silent, have encouraged police agencies to place a greater reliance on scientific investigative techniques.
   d. Advances in scientific technology have provided forensic scientists with many new skills and techniques to extract meaningful information from physical evidence.

10. Describe the advantages of incorporating an evidence collection unit into the organizational structure of the crime laboratory.

    Answer:
    a. Before evidence can be properly analyzed it must be recognized, collected, and properly packaged at the crime site.
    b. Evidence technicians under the continuous direction of the crime laboratory are more likely to have received thorough training in the gathering of evidence at the crime site.
    c. Evidence technicians, who are continuously exposed to the problems and techniques of the forensic scientist, are better prepared to adopt new procedures or modify existing procedures to improve evidence collection.

THE CRIME SCENE

LEARNING OBJECTIVES

1. Define physical evidence.
2. Discuss the responsibilities of the first police officer who arrives at a crime scene.
3. Explain the steps to be taken for thoroughly recording the crime scene.
4. Describe proper procedures for conducting a systematic search of crime scenes for physical evidence.
5. Describe proper techniques for packaging common types of physical evidence.
6. Define chain of custody.
7. Discuss the implications of the *Mincey* and *Tyler* cases.

GENERAL COMMENTS

Students should be referred to the Internet Web sites, "Crime-Scene Investigation" (http://police2.ucr.edu/csi.html) and "Evidence: The True Witness" [http://library.advanced.org/17049/gather/]. The latter site offers descriptions of relevant forensic science subjects and has an interactive game site to illustrate the role of forensic science in crime scene investigation. The "Crime-Scene Investigation" provides detailed guidelines and information regarding crime-scene response and the collection and preservation of physical evidence.

SUGGESTED EXPERIMENTS AND DEMONSTRATIONS

A mock crime scene can be set up in a classroom. Students are encouraged to become familiar with the proper packaging and handling of common types of physical evidence. Emphasize the preparation and use of the druggist fold. All pertinent information should be recorded in a notebook. Sketches may be made of the crime scene. A crime-scene sketch kit, which includes an excellent instructional manual on sketching, is available from Sirchie Laboratories, Raleigh, North Carolina.

SUGGESTED EXAMINATION QUESTIONS

_d_ 1. The obligation to maintain the integrity of evidence belongs to which of the following?
   a. The first police officer at the scene
   b. The forensic scientist
   c. The prosecutor
   d. The evidence clerk
   e. All of the above

_c_ 2. The relative evidential value of laboratory test results is almost always dependent on:
   a. The importance of the case
   b. The quantity of evidence submitted
   c. The way the evidence is collected and presented for examination
   d. The crime laboratory's caseload
   e. None of the above

_d_ 3. The manner of collecting and preserving physical evidence at a crime scene is determined by:
   a. The circumstance of the crime
   b. The importance of the case
   c. The number of evidence collectors present at the crime scene
   d. The nature of the evidence
   e. The availability of suitable packaging material

_d_ 4. Physical evidence may be obtained from:
   a. The crime scene
   b. The victim
   c. The suspect
   d. All of the above
   e. None of the above

5. The 1978 Supreme Court case which related to the impropriety of the warrantless collection of physical evidence at a homicide scene is _____. (*Mincey* v. *Arizona*)

_b_ 6. All of the following items may be placed in an airtight container except:
   a. Charred debris recovered from a fire
   b. Bloodstained clothing
   c. Glass
   d. Hairs and fibers
   e. Explosive residues

  _e_   7. The evidence collector is not concerned with:
       a. Maintaining the chain of custody
       b. Utilizing the proper packaging material for evidence
       c. Labeling evidence
       d. Collecting control specimens
       e. Determining the natural variations that exist in physi-
           cal evidence

       8. In cooperation with the medical examiner or coroner, what
           type of evidence is to be retrieved from a deceased victim for
           examination in the crime laboratory?

       Answer:
       a. clothing
       b. fingernail scrapings
       c. head and pubic hairs
       d. vaginal, anal, and oral swabs
       e. bullets
       f. hand swabs for gunshot residues

PHYSICAL EVIDENCE

LEARNING OBJECTIVES

1. List the common types of physical evidence encountered at crime scenes.
2. Explain the difference between the identification and comparison of physical evidence.
3. Define individual and class characteristics. Give examples of physical evidence possessing these characteristics.
4. Discuss the value of class evidence to a criminal investigation.
5. Explain the purpose physical evidence plays in reconstructing the events surrounding the commission of a crime.

SUGGESTED EXAMINATION QUESTIONS

a 1. Evidence having class characteristics can:
   a. Exonerate an innocent suspect
   b. Link a person to a crime with a high degree of certainty
   c. Always be fitted together in the manner of a jigsaw puzzle
   d. Have no evidential value
   e. None of the above

c 2. If the laboratory can piece broken glass from a window or headlight together, then the evidence has _____ characteristics.
   a. Identification
   b. Comparative
   c. Individual
   d. Class
   e. None of the above

a 3. A comparison analysis subjects a suspect specimen and a control specimen to the same tests and examinations for the ultimate purpose of determining:
   a. Whether or not they have a common origin
   b. If they are identical in chemical composition
   c. If the same person handled them
   d. If they are alike in molecular structure
   e. All of the above

4. Determining that an explosive mixture contains dynamite is an example of the process of _____. (identification)

5. A single-layer paint chip can normally be expected to have _____ characteristics. (class)

__d__   6. The "jigsaw fit" of known and questioned fragments is important for court presentation primarily because:
   a. It is a quick way of demonstrating how the object broke.
   b. Courts and juries are too nonscientific to understand it any other way.
   c. Instrumental analysis is too complicated to explain to nontechnical juries.
   d. This method will definitely demonstrate common origin when a match is made.
   e. Instrumental analysis of the fragments will not be sufficiently specific for comparison purposes.

__e__   7. Physical evidence that can be used to aid in a crime scene reconstruction include:
   a. Blood spatters
   b. Gunshot residues
   c. Glass fragments
   d. Shoeprints
   e. All of the above

8. List some of the advantages of class physical evidence.

   Answer:
   a. Provides corroboration of events based on objective scientific data.
   b. Often, the chances or odds of encountering two indistinguishable items of class physical evidence that actually originated from different sources are slight.
   c. When dealing with more than one type of class evidence, their collective presence may lead to an extremely high certainty that they originated from the same source.
   d. Physical evidence, whether it be individual or class, is accorded great weight in the courtroom.
   e. Class evidence may also serve to exonerate a person from a crime.

PHYSICAL PROPERTIES: GLASS AND SOIL

LEARNING OBJECTIVES

1. Define physical and chemical properties.
2. List and define the metric system's basic units and prefixes.
3. Compare metric and English units: length, volume, and mass.
4. Convert from one system of measurement to the other.
5. Distinguish between the Celsius and Fahrenheit temperature scales.
6. Distinguish mass from weight.
7. Define density.
8. Determine the density of irregular-shaped objects.
9. Define refractive index.
10. Distinguish crystalline from amorphous solids.
11. Define double refraction and birefringence.
12. Describe the dispersion of light through a prism.
13. Describe the flotation and immersion methods for comparing glass specimens.
14. State how to examine glass fractures to determine the direction of impact from a projectile.
15. Describe the proper collection of glass evidence.
16. List the important forensic properties of soil.
17. Describe the density-gradient tube technique.
18. Describe the proper collection of soil evidence.

SUGGESTED EXPERIMENTS AND DEMONSTRATIONS

The use of the triple-beam, top-loading, and single-pan analytical balances should be demonstrated. An interesting experiment that serves to introduce the student to the concept of density requires the determination of the density of an aluminum bar. Cylindrical aluminum bars are cut into sections weighing between 3 and 10 grams. The student first weighs the bar on a balance. The volume of a bar is determined by the amount of water it displaces in a graduated cylinder. The student should determine the densities of at least two aluminum bars of different sizes. The density of aluminum is 2.70 g/ml.

The comparative density of two window-glass chips can be demonstrated by the flotation technique. The density of a glass particle can be found by placing it in a test tube with a mixture of bromoform and bromobenzene. The particle remains suspended in the solution. A second particle is now added to the test tube and its ability to sink, float, or remain suspended is compared to the first particle. If both chips remain suspended, the closed tube may be heated and cooled to confirm that both sink and rise together. The glass chips must be clean and of approximately the same size.

The comparison of soil specimens by the density-gradient tube technique is a recommended laboratory exercise. I normally prepare four soil specimens, two of which originate from the same source. Each student is randomly assigned two soils for comparison. Two density-gradient columns are prepared by each student using glass tubing approximately 30 cm. in length and 6 to 10 mm. in diameter. Five layers are prepared by the student. The heaviest layer is pure tetrabromoethane, while the lightest is a 1:1 mixture of ethanol and tetrabromoethane. The intermediate layers are mixtures of the heavy and light liquids in the ratio of 3:1, 1:1, and 1:3, respectively.

SUGGESTED EXAMINATION QUESTIONS

_c_   1. The basic metric unit of volume is the:
   a. ounce
   b. meter
   c. liter
   d. cubic centimeter
   e. milliliter

_e_   2. One inch is equivalent to how many centimeters?
   a. 100
   b. 10
   c. 0.01
   d. 453.6
   e. 2.54

_d_   3. Water boils at:
   a. 0 Celsius
   b. 25 Celsius
   c. 50 Celsius
   d. 100 Celsius
   e. 212 Celsius

_e_   4. Which of the following is not a physical property of a substance?
   a. Boiling point
   b. Color
   c. Melting point
   d. Weight
   e. Color change in the presence of another chemical substance

_b_ 5. Density is defined as:
    a. Volume per unit weight
    b. Weight per unit volume
    c. Volume per unit volume
    d. Weight per unit weight
    e. None of the above

_b_ 6. A piece of glass is immersed in a liquid. It proceeds to float on the liquid's surface. This shows that the density of the glass is _____ the density of the liquid.
    a. More than
    b. Less than
    c. Equal to
    d. None of the above

_c_ 7. The two most important physical properties of glass for forensic comparisons are:
    a. color and density
    b. weight and density
    c. refractive index and density
    d. refractive index and weight
    e. refractive index and color

_a_ 8. The larger opening of a crater-shaped hole in glass made by the penetration of a projectile indicates:
    a. The exit side of the glass
    b. The entrance side of the glass
    c. That a bullet made the opening
    d. That the projectile was traveling at a low velocity
    e. None of the above

_c_ 9. If glass cannot be physically pieced together, then the control and question glass are best compared as to their:
    a. Color and density
    b. Weight and density
    c. Refractive index and density
    d. Refractive index and weight
    e. Refractive index and color

_c_ 10. The fracture pattern of glass usually has:
    a. Radial lines
    b. Concentric lines
    c. Radial and concentric lines
    d. Directional lines
    e. None of the above

_b_ 11. Stress marks on the edge of a radial crack near the point of impact are:
   a. Perpendicular to the side on which the force was applied
   b. Parallel to the side on which the force was applied
   c. Parallel to the side opposite the side on which the force was applied
   d. None of the above

_b_ 12. A technique frequently used to compare soils is:
   a. The immersion method
   b. Density-gradient tubes
   c. Flotation
   d. Becke Line
   e. Dispersion

13. A storefront window is broken and a robbery committed. A suspect is later found running from the scene. Examination of his shoes reveals glass particles embedded in a heel. Describe the proper collection and preservation of glass evidence for laboratory examination.
   A correct answer should stress the following points:
   a. The entire shoe is to be submitted for laboratory examination. The evidence collector is to avoid removing glass evidence from the shoe unless there is a distinct possibility that the glass will be lost in transit.
   b. Shoes are to be packaged in a box or paper bag and sent to the laboratory.
   c. A control glass from the broken window is to be submitted for laboratory examination. Normally a square-inch piece of glass will suffice.
   d. A pillbox, druggist fold, or vial are convenient containers for small glass fragments.
   e. All packages are to be properly labeled for identification. Minimal information should contain evidence collector's name or initials, the date, and sampling location. All items collected are to be described in the evidence collector's field notes.

14. A suspect has been found miles from the scene of a murder. Soil is found adhering to the suspect's shoe. Describe the proper collection and preservation of soil evidence that will permit a thorough comparison of the soil on the shoe to soil at the crime site.
   A correct answer should stress the following points:
   a. Do not remove soil from shoes. Each object that has soil on it is to be packaged in a leak proof container.
   b. Collect representative control soils at the crime scene and at various locations within a 100-yard radius of the scene. Package in solid containers or druggist folds.

c. Collect soil at all possible alibi locations the suspect may claim.

d. Collect approximately 1-2 tablespoons of soil, top layer only.

e. Label all specimens collected. Evidence collector's name or initials, the date, and sampling location are to be shown. All items collected are to be described in the evidence collector's field notes.

ORGANIC ANALYSIS

LEARNING OBJECTIVES

1. Define elements and compounds and give examples of each.
2. State the differences between a solid, liquid, and gas.
3. Define phase.
4. Distinguish between organic and inorganic compounds.
5. Distinguish between a qualitative and quantitative analysis.
6. Explain how a liquid reaches equilibrium with its gaseous phase as defined by Henry's Law.
7. Describe the process of chromatography.
8. Describe the parts of a gas chromatograph.
9. Define retention time.
10. Explain the difference between thin-layer and gas chromatography.
11. Define Rf value.
12. Describe electrophoresis.
13. State the differences between the wave and particle theories of light.
14. Describe the electromagnetic spectrum.
15. Explain the relationship between color and the selective absorption of light by molecules.
16. Define Beer's Law.
17. Name the parts of a simple absorption spectrophotometer.
18. Describe the utility of an ultraviolet and infrared absorption spectrum for the identification of organic compounds.
19. Describe the concept of mass spectrometry
20. Describe the significance of a mass spectrum.

SUGGESTED DEMONSTRATIONS AND EXPERIMENTS

I have found that running a thin-layer during the lecture aids the class in understanding the concept of chromatography. I like to use a chloroform extract of marijuana to illustrate TLC. A precoated silica gel plate is used. The developing solvent is toluene, and the visualizer is an aqueous solution of Fast Blue B salt. However, possession of a controlled dangerous substance, such as marijuana, is lawful only when a Drug Enforcement Administration registration number is obtained and necessary state and local requirements are fulfilled.

A demonstration of the operation of a gas chromatograph and the infrared spectrophotometer should supplement lecture material relating to these instrumental techniques. During a laboratory session I have had good luck with a prepackaged TLC experiment marketed by Lab-Aids Inc., 17 Colt Court, Ronkonkoma, N.Y. 11779. Using the thin-layer chromatography kit (Lab-Aids catalog no. 17), each student will run chromatograms of five different sample dye solutions in order to establish standards and then two chromatograms of two unknowns. This approach gives each student an opportunity to appreciate the usefulness of TLC.

SUGGESTED EXAMINATION QUESTIONS

_c_   1.   Which of the following is an element?
    a. Wood
    b. Water
    c. Aluminum
    d. Air
    e. Fire

_a_   2.   The physical state that has both shape and volume is a:
    a. Solid
    b. Liquid
    c. Gas
    d. Vapor
    e. All of these

_e_   3.   Which of the following is false?
    a. The basic building blocks of all substances are elements.
    b. Elements are composed of atoms.
    c. Two or more elements combine to form compounds.
    d. Compounds are composed of molecules.
    e. At present, 106 compounds have been identified.

_d_   4.   Organic chemistry is the study of substances containing the element:
    a. Hydrogen
    b. Oxygen
    c. Nitrogen
    d. Carbon
    e. Silicon

_c_   5.   A technique for separating and tentatively identifying the components of a mixture is:
    a. Spectrophotometry
    b. Infrared
    c. Chromatography
    d. Mass spectrometry
    e. Ultraviolet

_c_   6. Which of the following is not part of the gas chromatograph?
- a. Injection port
- b. Column
- c. Slit
- d. Flame detector
- e. Recorder

_d_   7. Which of the following is not part of the absorption spectrophotometer?
- a. Slit
- b. Monochromator
- c. Recorder
- d. Carrier gas
- e. Source

_d_   8. A compound can tentatively be identified by gas chromatography from its:
- a. Carrier gas
- b. Rf value
- c. Partition coefficient
- d. Retention time
- e. Peak height

_a_   9. A single specific test for identification is:
- a. Infrared spectrophotometry
- b. Ultraviolet spectrophotometry
- c. Gas chromatography
- d. Thin-layer chromatography
- e. Density-gradient tubes

_a_   10. The last step in a thin-layer chromatographic analysis is:
- a. Visualization
- b. Spotting the unknown
- c. Spotting a standard
- d. Developing the plate in an enclosed tank
- e. Drying the plate

_d_   11. The function of a monochromator is to:
- a. Disperse light into its different wavelengths
- b. Pass the radiation through a slit
- c. Select radiation of known frequency or wavelength
- d. All of the above
- e. None of the above

_d_ 12. The distribution of a substance between a mobile and stationary phase describes:
   a. Spectrophotometry
   b. Dispersion
   c. Density-gradient tubes
   d. Chromatography
   e. Mass spectrometry

_c_ 13. The recorder of a spectrophotometer measures:
   a. The Rf value of light
   b. The retention time of light
   c. Absorption of light at specific frequencies
   d. The refractive index of light
   e. The speed of light

_e_ 14. Which of the following has higher frequencies and higher energy values in the electromagnetic spectrum?
   a. Visible light
   b. Radio waves
   c. Ultraviolet radiation
   d. Infrared radiation
   e. X-rays

_d_ 15. Which of the following statements is false?
   a. A gas chromatograph can be coupled to a mass spectrometer.
   b. Gas chromatography cannot produce a specific identification of a chemical substance.
   c. In mass spectrometry, a chemical substance enters a chamber where it's fragmented by high-energy electrons.
   d. Many chemical substances have similar mass spectra fragmentation patterns.
   e. A mass spectrometer can detect materials weighing only one millionth of a gram.

INORGANIC ANALYSIS

LEARNING OBJECTIVES

1. Describe the usefulness of trace elements for the forensic comparison of various types of physical evidence.
2. Distinguish between a continuous and line emission spectrum.
3. Describe the parts of a simple emission spectrograph.
4. List the parts of a simple atomic absorption spectrophotometer.
5. Define protons, neutrons, and electrons, including their mass and charge relationships.
6. Define atomic number and atomic mass number.
7. Describe the orbital energy levels that are occupied by electrons.
8. State what happens when an atom absorbs a definite amount of energy.
9. Explain the phenomenon of an atom releasing energy in the form of light.
10. Define an isotope.
11. Define radioactivity.
12. Explain how elements can be made radioactive.
13. Describe why an X-ray diffraction pattern is useful for chemical identification.

SUGGESTED EXPERIMENTS AND DEMONSTRATIONS

Atomic emission spectra can be demonstrated with the use of a simple diffraction grating spectroscope. The chloride salts of lithium, calcium, strontium, copper, barium, and potassium can produce characteristic line spectra. Dip a loop of a clean nichrome wire into each salt (moistened with a few drops of 6M HCl) and place it in a small blue Bunsen flame. Also, the student should use the spectroscope to look at a tungsten filament lamp and a hydrogen discharge tube.

SUGGESTED EXAMINATION QUESTIONS

__a__ 1. The most abundant element of the earth's crust is:
   a. Oxygen
   b. Hydrogen
   c. Carbon
   d. Aluminum
   e. Silicon

__d__ 2. A "fingerprint" of an element is obtained by the technique of:
   a. Infrared spectrophotometry
   b. Ultraviolet spectrophotometry
   c. Gas chromatography
   d. Emission spectroscopy
   e. Thin-layer chromatography

__d__ 3. Which of the following statements is false?
   a. Protons and neutrons compose the nucleus of an atom.
   b. The proton has a charge of plus one.
   c. The neutron has no electrical charge.
   d. The electron and proton have the same mass.
   e. An atom has an equal number of protons and electrons.

__e__ 4. The atoms of hydrogen, deuterium, and tritium all have the same number of protons, but differ in the number of neutrons they possess. These substances are:
   a. Elements
   b. Compounds
   c. Molecules
   d. Radioactive
   e. Isotopes

__d__ 5. In neutron activation analysis, an element is identified by measuring the energy of emitting:
   a. Protons
   b. Electrons
   c. Neutrons
   d. Gamma rays
   e. Alpha rays

__e__ 6. Gamma rays are:
   a. Electrons
   b. Protons
   c. Neutrons
   d. Alpha particles
   e. Electromagnetic radiation

__b__ 7. Which of the following statements is correct?
   a. All atoms of an element have the same atomic mass number.
   b. All atoms of an element have the same number of protons.
   c. All atoms of an element have the same number of neutrons.
   d. The number of protons in the nucleus of an atom is called the atomic mass number.
   e. All atoms of an element have an equal number of neutrons and electrons.

<u>b</u>   8. The technique commonly used to identify crystalline sub-
        stances is:
        a. Atomic absorption spectrophotometry
        b. X-ray diffraction
        c. Emission spectroscopy
        d. Neutron activation analysis
        e. Ultraviolet spectrophotometry

<u>d</u>   9. The emission spectrograph is used to determine:
        a. The mass of a substance
        b. The weight of a substance
        c. The crystalline structure of a substance
        d. The elemental composition of a substance
        e. All of the above

THE MICROSCOPE

LEARNING OBJECTIVES

1. List the parts of the compound microscope.
2. Define magnification, field of view, working distance, and depth of focus.
3. Describe the comparison microscope.
4. List the advantages of the stereoscopic microscope.
5. Define plane-polarized light.
6. Describe how a polarizing microscope is designed to detect polarized light.
7. Explain the advantages of linking a microscope to a spectrophotometer from the forensic scientist's point-of-view.
8. Give examples of how a microspectrophotometer can be utilized to examine trace physical evidence.
9. Compare the mechanism for image formation of a light microscope to that of the scanning electron microscope.
10. List the advantages and some forensic applications of the scanning electron microscope.

SUGGESTED EXPERIMENTS

Because of the importance of the microscope to the crime laboratory, a criminalistics course must stress the use of these instruments. Each student should have access to a compound and stereoscopic microscope, and possibly a comparison microscope. The proper handling and care of the microscope are to be emphasized in the laboratory. Exercises demonstrating the magnifying power and depth of field of the microscope are most suitable for introducing the student to this instrument. Observing specimens like tea and tobacco under the stereoscopic microscope allows the student to gain an appreciation for the stereo's great depth of field. The student must also learn how to prepare dry and wet mount slides for examination under the compound microscope.

SUGGESTED EXAMINATION QUESTIONS

_e_ 1. The magnification power of a microscope equals the magnifying power of:
   a. The eyepiece lens
   b. The objective lens
   c. The objective lens multiplied by two
   d. The eyepiece lens multiplied by two
   e. The objective lens multiplied by the eyepiece lens

_b_   2.   The microscope examination of a bullet requires:
    a.   Transmitted light
    b.   Reflected light
    c.   Condensed light
    d.   All of the above
    e.   None of the above

_e_   3.   Which of these is not part of the optical system of a compound microscope?
    a.   Abbe condenser
    b.   Objective lens
    c.   Eyepiece lens
    d.   The illuminator
    e.   The body tube

_a_   4.   Which of the following statements is false?
    a.   If the polarizer and analyzer of a polarizing microscope are placed parallel to each other, no light will penetrate.
    b.   Light confined to a single plane of vibration is said to be polarized.
    c.   Many crystals are birefringent.
    d.   The lens nearest the specimen is called the objective lens.
    e.   A compound microscope produces a virtual image.

_b_   5.   The most important tool of the firearms examiner is the:
    a.   Compound microscope
    b.   Comparison microscope
    c.   Stereoscopic microscope
    d.   Polarizing microscope
    e.   Scanning electron microscope

_e_   6.   Which of the following is false?
    a.   The scanning electron microscope (SEM) produces an image by aiming a beam of electrons onto a specimen.
    b.   The major attraction of the SEM is its high magnification and depth of field.
    c.   The SEM produces an image that is stereoscopic in appearance.
    d.   A SEM can be fitted with an analyzer capable of identifying the elements present in the specimen under examination.
    e.   Microwaves are generated when the electron beam of the SEM strikes a target.

7. Match each of the following descriptions to the choices listed below:

a.	Magnification	g.	Stereoscopic microscope
b.	Working distance	h.	Transmitted illumination
c.	Polarizing microscope	i.	Vertical illumination
d.	Depth of focus	j.	Comparison microscope
e.	Field of view	k.	Objective lens
f.	Real image	l.	Virtual image

1. Space between the specimen and objective lens.   _b_

2. Presents a distinctive three-dimensional image.   _g_

3. Illumination required to view a transparent object.   _h_

4. Eyepiece multiplied by objective lens.   _a_

5. The thickness of a specimen in focus.   _d_

6. Size of the specimen area being observed.   _e_

7. Provides a simultaneous view of two specimens.   _j_

8. Used to examine birefringent materials.   _c_

9. The image seen through a compound microscope.   _l_

Hairs, Fibers, and Paint

Learning Objectives

1. Describe the cuticle, cortex, and medulla of hair.
2. Describe the three phases of hair growth.
3. Explain the distinction between animal and human hairs.
4. List hair features that are useful for the comparison of human hairs.
5. Explain the proper collection of hair evidence.
6. Describe the role of DNA typing in hair comparisons
7. Classify fibers.
8. Describe the structure of a polymer.
9. List the properties of fibers that are most useful for forensic comparisons.
10. Describe the proper collection of fiber evidence.
11. Describe the components of paint.
12. Classify automobile paints.
13. List those examinations most useful for performing a forensic comparison of paint.
14. Describe the proper collection and preservation of paint evidence.

Suggested Experiments

An effective demonstration of the variability of hair over the human scalp is to have your students compare at least 6-8 hairs that have been wet mounted. Upon completion of the examination, the class is asked to estimate the number of individuals that contributed to the hair collection. Of course, the collection consists of hair from only one individual. The instructor should compile at least 24 hair mounts from one person for this experiment. Additionally, each student is to examine his or her own scalp hair using a glycerin wet mount. Students should also be encouraged to bring in hair from household pets for examination.

Instructors should obtain the CD-ROM database for common animal hairs from RJ Lee Group, Inc., 350 Hochberg Rd., Monroeville, Pa. 15146. Students should be given opportunity to familiarize themselves with the applicability of this database to forensic hair analysis.

An instructor may want to prepare small fragments of automobile paint mixed in with other debris for examination under the stereoscopic microscope. The objective of the experiment is to identify the probable make and model of the automobile from the paint's color and solubility in acetone.

SUGGESTED EXAMINATION QUESTIONS

__b__   1. The portion of the hair containing its scales is:
   a. The cortex
   b. The cuticle
   c. The medulla
   d. The root
   e. The follicle

__d__   2. A human head hair is best characterized by:
   a. The absence of a cortex
   b. Its scale pattern
   c. A medulla that is more than 1/2 the overall diameter of the hair shaft
   d. A medulla that is absent or is less than 1/3 the overall diameter of the hair shaft
   e. A continuous or interrupted medulla

__c__   3. Hair can best be characterized as originating from an animal by examining:
   a. The medulla
   b. The cuticle
   c. Both the medulla and cuticle
   d. Its color
   e. Its scale structure

__e__   4. Which statement is true?
   a. The racial origin of hair can always be identified.
   b. Hair can be individualized through its trace elemental composition.
   c. Hair is routinely examined to determine sex.
   d. A single hair can be individualized to one person.
   e. Two hairs from the same head may not have the same morphological characteristics.

__d__   5. Rayon is classified as a:
   a. Natural fiber
   b. Synthetic fiber
   c. Plant fiber
   d. Regenerated fiber
   e. Animal fiber

_e_   6. Which of the following properties should be examined when comparing two fibers?
   a. Color
   b. Diameter
   c. Birefringence
   d. The presence or absence of delustering particles
   e. All of the above

_c_   7. Paint chips may be individualized to a single source by examining their:
   a. Infrared spectra
   b. Ultraviolet spectra
   c. Color and layer structure
   d. Pyrograms
   e. Their relative size

_e_   8. The polymeric make-up of paint binders can readily be compared by:
   a. Emission spectroscopy
   b. Thin-layer chromatography
   c. Microscopy
   d. Layer structure
   e. Pyrolysis gas chromatography

_b_   9. Automobile finishes typically contain which layers?
   a. Colorcoat
   b. An electrocoat, primers, colorcoat, and clearcoat
   c. Clearcoat
   d. Electrocoat primer and colorcoat
   e. None of the above

10. Describe the proper collection and preservation of paint evidence from an automobile suspected of being involved in a hit-and-run incident. Paint that is foreign to the suspect automobile is observed on the hood. A proper answer should include the following points:
   a. Scrape the foreign paint as well as all underlying layers of paint off the car's surface using a clean knife or scalpel. The scraping must clearly show the layer structure of the paint.
   b. Obtain a control paint sample from an adjacent undamaged area of the car. Again, all layers must be included.
   c. Package each paint specimen separately in a proper container. A druggist fold or a vial makes an excellent container.
   d. Label all specimen containers. Evidence collector's name or initials, the date, and the sampling location are to be shown. All items collected are to be described in the evidence collector's field notes.

DRUGS

LEARNING OBJECTIVES

1. Define psychological and physical dependence.
2. Name and classify the commonly abused drugs.
3. Describe the tendency to develop psychological and physical dependency for the more commonly abused drugs.
4. Describe the schedules of the Controlled Substances Act.
5. Describe the laboratory tests that forensic chemists normally rely upon to comprise a routine drug identification scheme.
6. Explain the testing procedures utilized for the forensic identification of marijuana.
7. Discuss the proper collection and preservation of drug evidence.

SUGGESTED EXPERIMENTS AND DEMONSTRATIONS

A favorite experiment of mine is to have students examine unknown vegetative mixtures for the presence of marijuana. This examination is conducted with the aid of a stereoscopic microscope. The vegetative preparations are composed of marijuana, catnip, and oregano.

A number of alternatives are available for demonstrating laboratory techniques that are used for drug identification. I would recommend emphasizing the application of color tests and TLC to drug analysis. Drug standards exempted from Drug Enforcement Administration licensing requirements can be obtained from various suppliers: e.g., Alltech Inc., Deerfield, Il. and Sigma Chemical Co., St. Louis, Mo.

SUGGESTED EXAMINATION QUESTIONS

__a__ 1. The reagent used for the field test of heroin is:
   a. Marquis
   b. Duquenois-Levine
   c. Scott reagent
   d. Van Urk
   e. Sodium acetate

__d__ 2. Marijuana is considered to be a:
   a. Depressant
   b. Stimulant
   c. Narcotic
   d. Hallucinogen
   e. Tranquilizer

_e_ 3. The most satisfactory way of simultaneously separating and tentatively identifying drugs is by:
   a. Ultraviolet spectrophotometry
   b. Infrared spectrophotometry
   c. Emission spectroscopy
   d. Neutron activation analysis
   e. Chromatography

_b_ 4. Drugs deemed to have the highest potential for abuse and having a current medical use are listed in which schedule of the Controlled Substances Act?
   a. I
   b. II
   c. III
   d. IV
   e. V

_b_ 5. The most common diluent of heroin is:
   a. Mannitol
   b. Quinine
   c. Procaine
   d. Starch
   e. Methapyrilene

_b_ 6. A police officer performs a field test on a white powder, obtaining a purple color. The most likely drug present is:
   a. Cocaine
   b. Heroin
   c. LSD
   d. Methadone
   e. A barbiturate

_c_ 7. There is a significant likelihood that continued use of _____ will result in a low degree of psychological dependence:
   a. Cocaine
   b. Heroin
   c. Marijuana
   d. Barbiturates
   e. Amphetamines

_e_ 8. Regular use of the following drug may lead to physical dependency:
   a. LSD
   b. Marijuana
   c. Aspirin
   d. Caffeine
   e. Ethyl alcohol

_d_   9. Which of the following is not a stimulant?
    a. Caffeine
    b. Amphetamine
    c. Cocaine
    d. Ethyl alcohol
    e. All of the above are stimulants.

_a_   10. Heroin is a chemical derivative of:
    a. Morphine
    b. Barbituric acid
    c. Codeine
    d. Methadone
    e. Amphetamine

_d_   11. The following analytical technique is considered to be a specific test in a drug identification scheme:
    a. Color test
    b. Microcrystalline test
    c. Thin-layer chromatography
    d. Infrared spectrophotometry
    e. Ultraviolet spectrophotometry

_b_   12. Which of the following is synthetically produced and does not occur naturally?
    a. Cocaine
    b. Amphetamine
    c. Morphine
    d. Opium
    e. Ethyl alcohol

_e_   13. Which of the following is not a depressant?
    a. Librium
    b. Valium
    c. Methaqualone
    d. Ethyl alcohol
    e. All of the above are depressants.

_d_   14. Which of the following statements is false?
    a. Hashish is a concentrated preparation of marijuana.
    b. The active ingredient of marijuana is tetrahydro-cannabinol.
    c. Prior to 1970 marijuana was classified as a narcotic drug.
    d. Marijuana is synthesized from the Cannabis sativa plant.
    e. Marijuana can tentatively be identified by the Duquenois-Levine color test.

_e_ 15. Which of the following is considered to be a hallucinogen?
a. Phencyclidine (PCP)
b. Mescaline
c. Psilocybin
d. STP
e. All of the above are hallucinogens.

_d_ 16. The tranquilizers Valium and Librium are classified in which schedule of the Controlled Substances Act?
a. I
b. II
c. III
d. IV
e. V

FORENSIC TOXICOLOGY

LEARNING OBJECTIVES

1. Explain how alcohol is absorbed into the bloodstream, transported throughout the body, and finally eliminated by oxidation and excretion.
2. Name the important parts of the human circulatory system.
3. Describe the process by which alcohol is excreted in the breath via the alveoli sacs.
4. Describe the design of the Breathalyzer.
5. Explain the significance of a chemical equation.
6. Explain the concept of an infrared breath-testing device.
7. Demonstrate some common field sobriety tests.
8. List common laboratory procedures for measuring alcohol's concentration in the blood.
9. Describe the precautions to be taken to properly preserve blood for analysis for its alcohol content.
10. What is the presumptive impairment level for blood alcohol in your state?
11. Explain the significance of the implied consent law and the *Schmerber* v. *California* case to traffic enforcement.
12. Define acid and base.
13. Develop an appreciation for the role of the toxicologist in the criminal justice system.
14. Describe some of the techniques that forensic toxicologists use for isolating and identifying drugs and poisons.
15. Discuss the significance of finding a drug in human tissues and organs.
16. Discuss how best the Drug Recognition Expert and the forensic toxicologist can coordinate their efforts to support the significance of a positive drug finding.

SUGGESTED DEMONSTRATIONS

Students should become familiar with the operation of a breath-testing device. One interesting demonstration involving a breath tester requires a student to rinse his or her mouth with some 80-90 proof liquor without swallowing the beverage. The subject is then tested on the breath tester 10, 15, and 20 minutes from the time the liquor is removed from the mouth. The breath-test reading of the subject will be zero after 20 minutes. Traces of alcohol in the mouth will produce excessively high readings. It takes 20 minutes for mouth alcohol to dissipate. For this reason, a properly conducted breath test requires that a subject be observed for 20 minutes prior to the administration of a breath test in order to verify that no oral intake of alcohol has occurred during this period of time.

Suggested Examination Questions

<u>d</u>   1. Alcohol is eliminated from the body chemically unchanged in:
   a. Urine
   b. Breath
   c. Perspiration
   d. All of the above
   e. None of the above

<u>c</u>   2. Alcohol is oxidized in the body primarily in:
   a. The stomach
   b. The small intestine
   c. The liver
   d. The lungs
   e. The kidneys

<u>c</u>   3. The blood alcohol concentration level for being presumed to be legally "Under the Influence" in most states is:
   a. 0.05% or greater
   b. 0.08% or greater
   c. 0.10% or greater
   d. 0.13% or greater
   e. 0.15% or greater

<u>a</u>   4. A breath test may be used to analyze:
   a. Ethyl alcohol
   b. Marijuana
   c. Barbiturates
   d. Amphetamines
   e. All of the above

<u>c</u>   5. Blood is drawn from a living suspect involved in an automobile accident. If the specimen is kept unrefrigerated and at a moderately warm temperature, the alcohol concentration can be expected to:
   a. Remain unchanged
   b. Increase with time
   c. Decrease with time
   d. Either increase or decrease with time
   e. Outcome is unpredictable.

_c_ 6. The elimination or "burn off" rate of alcohol averages is
_____% w/v per hour.
   a. 0.10
   b. 0.15
   c. 0.0l5
   d. 0.0l0
   e. None of the above

_d_ 7. The ratio of alcohol in the blood to alcohol in alveoli air is
approximately:
   a. 500 to one
   b. 1000 to one
   c. 1050 to one
   d. 2100 to one
   e. 4200 to one

_d_ 8. The following statement is false:
   a. Alcohol is broken down in the liver by oxidation.
   b. Alcohol can be considered a brain depressant.
   c. Alcohol is distributed nearly evenly throughout water
portions of the body by blood.
   d. The Breathalyzer measures the absorption of light by
alcohol.
   e. Methanol (wood alcohol) and isopropyl alcohol (rubbing
alcohol) are much more toxic than ethyl alcohol.

_a_ 9. The analytical technique widely used for directly measuring
the amount of alcohol present in the blood is:
   a. Gas chromatography
   b. Thin-layer chromatography
   c. Infrared spectrophotometry
   d. Atomic absorption
   e. Neutron activation analysis

_c_ 10. Field sobriety tests that can be employed to ascertain the
degree of an individual's alcohol impairment normally do
not include the following:
   a. Portable, roadside breath tester
   b. Horizontal gaze nystagmus
   c. Gas chromatography
   d. Walk and turn
   e. One-leg stand

_b_   11. The following drug is not found in blood or urine:
  a. Morphine
  b. Heroin
  c. Amphetamine
  d. Methadone
  e. Amobarbital

_d_   12. A neutral substance will have a pH closest to:
  a. 0
  b. 2
  c. 5
  d. 7
  e. 9

_b_   13. For the purpose of extracting the drug out of body tissues, an amphetamine is classified as a/an:
  a. Acid drug
  b. Basic drug
  c. Neutral drug
  d. All of the above
  e. None of the above

_b_   14. Carbon monoxide combines with what component of blood?
  a. Carboxyhemoglobin
  b. Hemoglobin
  c. Oxyhemoglobin
  d. White blood cells
  e. The plasma

_e_   15. In the case of *Schmerber* v. *California*, blood was categorized as being:
  a. Direct evidence
  b. Indirect evidence
  c. Circumstantial evidence
  d. Testimonial evidence
  e. Non-testimonial evidence

_d_   16. The Breathalyzer measures the quantity of light absorbed by:
  a. Sulfuric acid
  b. Silver nitrate
  c. Acetone
  d. Potassium dichromate
  e. Ethyl alcohol

<u>c</u>   17. Some breath-testing devices for alcohol use _____
          light to measure the quantity of alcohol trapped in a chamber:
   a. Visible
   b. Ultraviolet
   c. Infrared
   d. Colored
   e. Laser

<u>d</u>   18. In forensic toxicology, all positive drug findings must be con-
          firmed by a specific chemical test. The confirmation test of
          choice is:
   a. Ultraviolet spectrophotometry
   b. Gas chromatography
   c. Infrared spectrophotometry
   d. Gas chromatography-mass spectrometry
   e. Thin-layer chromatography

     19. The Drug Recognition Expert evaluation process can suggest
          the presence of how many broad categories of drugs?
          (Answer: 7)

FORENSIC ASPECTS OF ARSON AND EXPLOSION INVESTIGATIONS

LEARNING OBJECTIVES

1. Define oxidation.
2. Define energy and give examples of its different forms.
3. Describe the role of heat energy in chemical reactions.
4. Define heat of combustion and ignition temperature.
5. Describe the difference between an exothermic and endothermic chemical reaction.
6. Explain why the oxidation of iron to rust is not accompanied by a flaming fire.
7. List the requirements necessary to initiate and sustain combustion.
8. Describe how physical evidence must be collected at the scene of a suspected arson or explosion.
9. Describe laboratory procedures used for the detection and identification of hydrocarbon and explosive residues.
10. Explain how explosives are classified.
11. Explain the differences between an initiating and non-initiating explosive.
12. List some common commercial, homemade, and military explosives.
13. List some common laboratory tests employed for the detection of explosives.

SUGGESTED DEMONSTRATIONS

The gas chromatographic analysis of gasoline makes for an interesting demonstration. I would recommend using a packed or capillary non-polar silicone column. Gasoline is placed in a vial covered with a rubber septum. Remove 1-2 cc. of air above the liquid with a syringe for injection into the GC. Refer to the text for the resultant chromatograms.

SUGGESTED EXAMINATION QUESTIONS

<u>d</u>   1. Which of the following statements is true?
  a. All chemical reactions give off heat.
  b. Heat is required to change one element into another.
  c. A chemical equation shows the number of atoms lost during a chemical reaction.
  d. Oxidations are chemical reactions that give off heat.
  e. Oxidation reactions always produce a fire.

<u>b</u>   2. The chemical reaction associated with a fire is:
  a. Reduction
  b. Oxidation
  c. Precipitation
  d. Acid-base
  e. None of the above

<u>d</u>   3. A natural heat-producing process that may give rise to a fire is:
  a. A chain reaction
  b. Flash point
  c. Ignition point
  d. Spontaneous combustion
  e. Glowing combustion

<u>d</u>   4. The minimum temperature at which fuel vapor will ignite is known as:
  a. The glow temperature
  b. The boiling point
  c. The flash point
  d. The ignition temperature
  e. The vapor temperature

<u>c</u>   5. Gasoline residues are best characterized by:
  a. Ultraviolet analysis
  b. Infrared spectrophotometry
  c. Gas chromatography
  d. Emission spectroscopy
  e. Atomic absorption

_c_ 6. Which of the following is not possible to determine from a laboratory examination of evidence recovered from an arson?
  a. The presence of gasoline, kerosene, or turpentine in debris.
  b. Liquid gasolines may be compared for origin.
  c. Examination of the debris may reveal the brand name of gasoline used to start the fire.
  d. The criminalist may be able to reconstruct the ignition mechanism used by the arsonist.
  e. All of the above are possible to accomplish.

_a_ 7. An initiating explosive often used in detonators is:
  a. Lead azide
  b. PETN
  c. TNT
  d. Dynamite
  e. Nitrocellulose

_d_ 8. The chemical ingredients of black powder are commonly:
  a. Aluminum, potassium, nitrate, nitrocellulose
  b. Sulfur, carbon, nitrogen
  c. Carbon, nitrocellulose, potassium chlorate
  d. Potassium nitrate, carbon, sulfur
  e. None of the above

_e_ 9. Which of the following statements is false?
  a. Potassium chlorate can be mixed with sulfuric acid and sugar to create a low explosive.
  b. Chemicals that supply oxygen are known as oxidizing agents.
  c. Thin-layer chromatography is a useful analytical technique for screening debris for explosive residues.
  d. Smokeless powder is a low explosive.
  e. Dynamite is an initiating high explosive.

_e_ 10. Which of the following is not a military explosive?
  a. RDX
  b. C-4
  c. PETN
  d. TNT
  e. Nitroglycerin

    11. Discuss the proper collection of evidence at the origin of a fire that is suspected of being initiated by gasoline. Describe the proper submission of controls for laboratory examination. A proper answer should include the following points.
  a. Nothing at the suspected origin of the fire must be touched or moved before notes, sketches, and photographs are taken.

b. All material suspected of containing flammable residues must be packaged in an airtight container, such as a clean paint can.

c. Collect two or three quarts of ash and soot debris at the fire's origin. The collection must include all porous materials suspected of containing flammable residues. A portable hydrocarbon detector, as well as a sense of smell, can aid in the proper selection of suspect materials.

d. Similar but uncontaminated materials from another area of the structure must be collected to serve as controls.

e. Label all specimen containers. The evidence collector's name or initials, the date, and the sampling location are to be shown. All items collected are to be described in the evidence collector's field notes.

FORENSIC SEROLOGY

LEARNING OBJECTIVES

1. List the A-B-O antigens and antibodies found in the blood for each of the four blood types: A, B, AB, and O.
2. Explain why agglutination occurs.
3. Explain how whole blood is typed.
4. Describe tests used to characterize a stain as blood.
5. Explain the significance of the precipitin test to forensic serology.
6. Describe the absorption-elution technique.
7. Describe how the existence of polymorphic enzymes and proteins contributes to blood's individualization.
8. Define chromosome and gene.
9. How is the Punnet square used to determine the genotypes and phenotypes of offspring?
10. List the laboratory tests necessary to characterize seminal stains.
11. Explain how suspect stains are to be properly preserved for laboratory examination.
12. Describe the collection of physical evidence related to a rape investigation.

SUGGESTED EXPERIMENTS AND DEMONSTRATIONS

Procedures utilized for typing dried blood are much too detailed and time consuming to be incorporated into a course of this scope. However, the typing of whole blood is an experiment that illustrates some important points covered in the chapter. Blood-typing kits which allow each student to safely determine his or her own blood type are available from several scientific supply companies. This kit should include anti-A, anti-B, and anti-D sera.

A presumptive test reagent for blood is prepared by adding phenolphthalein (4 g), potassium hydroxide (40 g), and zinc dust (20 g) to distilled water (200 ml). The mixture is boiled until the pink coloration has practically disappeared, cooled, and stored in a refrigerator. Before use, an aliquot of stock solution is diluted with an equal volume of ethyl alcohol. Any suspicious stain is lightly rubbed with dry filter paper. A drop of the phenolphthalein reagent and a drop of hydrogen peroxide (3% w/v) is put on the paper. A deep pink color indicates a positive reaction.

Commercially prepared presumptive blood testing reagents and kits can be purchased from Doje's Incorp., P.O. Box 500, Ocoee, Fla., 407-880-8149.

A presumptive test reagent for semen is prepared by adding glacial acetic acid (10 ml) to distilled water (200 ml). Anhydrous sodium acetate (24 g), sodium alpha-napthylphosphate (2 g), and Fast Blue B dye (2 g) are then dissolved to produce the reagent. This is stored in a refrigerator and filtered before use. A suspect stain is rubbed lightly with moistened filter paper and a drop of the reagent is added to the paper. A purple color indicates a positive reaction.

SUGGESTED EXAMINATION QUESTIONS

  c   1. The presence or absence of how many antigens determines an individual's blood type in the A-B-O system?
   a. 0
   b. 1
   c. 2
   d. 3
   e. 4

  d   2. What approximate percentage of the population is type B?
   a. 80%
   b. 41%
   c. 38%
   d. 15%
   e. 6%

  d   3. An individual who is type O has:
   a. 0 antibodies
   b. A antibodies
   c. B antibodies
   d. Both A and B antibodies
   e. Neither A nor B antibodies

  d   4. Antibodies are found:
   a. On the red blood cells
   b. On the white blood cells
   c. In the solid portion of blood
   d. In the blood serum
   e. In fibrinogen

  e   5. A precipitin test can be used to identify:
   a. Human blood
   b. Dog blood
   c. Cat blood
   d. Mouse blood
   e. All of the above

 c   6. If blood is found to have both A and B antigens, it is typed as:
        a. A
        b. B
        c. AB
        d. O
        e. Rh positive

 c   7. One parent is type AB; the other parent is type O. A possible genotype for an offspring is:
        a. AB
        b. OO
        c. AO
        d. All of the above
        e. None of the above

 a   8. What approximate percentage of the population is secretors?
        a. 80%
        b. 41%
        c. 38%
        d. 15%
        e. 6%

 e   9. Which of the following can be typed by the A-B-O system?
        a. Skin
        b. Semen
        c. Saliva
        d. Blood
        e. All of the above

 c   10. Which of the following statements is false?
        a. Semen is unequivocally identified by the presence of spermatozoa.
        b. The likelihood of finding seminal acid phosphatase in vaginal swabs decreases with time.
        c. Spermatozoa can generally be found in the vagina of a living female after three days.
        d. Semen may contain A and B antigens.
        e. The enzyme PGM is normally found in human semen.

 e   11. A stain can tentatively be identified as blood by:
        a. The benzidine test
        b. The luminol test
        c. The phenolphthalein test
        d. The Takayama test
        e. All of the above

_d_   12.   Which of the following statements is false?
- a.   Dried bloodstains may be typed by the absorption elution technique.
- b.   All bloods contain the enzyme peroxidase.
- c.   The enzyme PGM is present in all human blood.
- d.   The benzidine test is used to determine whether blood is of human origin.
- e.   The bonding of an antigen with its specific antibody causes agglutination.

_b_   13.   Acid-phosphatase is a major constituent of:
- a.   Blood
- b.   Semen
- c.   Saliva
- d.   Perspiration
- e.   All of the above

_c_   14.   The presence of _____ proves that a stain is seminal in nature:
- a.   PGM
- b.   Acid phosphatase
- c.   p30
- d.   DNA
- e.   A-B-O antigens

_b_   15.   If type A blood is found in approximately 42 percent of the population and the PGM 2-1 blood type found in approximately 36 percent of the population, what percentage of the population will have blood with types A and PGM 2-1?
- a.   30%
- b.   15%
- c.   1.5%
- d.   42%
- e.   36%

   16.   The dead victim of a rape is found in her apartment. Describe the proper collection and preservation of the seminal stained clothing. Emphasize the proper collection of controls from the victim and suspect.
   A proper answer should include the following points:
- a.   Each article of the victim's clothing must be separately wrapped and placed in a well-ventilated container. Other items suspected of containing semen must be packaged in a similar manner. Refrigerate the container or store it in a cool location out of direct sunlight until delivery to the laboratory.
- b.   The evidence collector must handle the clothing with a minimal amount of personal contact. All body fluids must be assumed to be infectious; hence, wearing dis-

posable latex gloves while handling the evidence is required. Latex gloves will also significantly reduce the possibility that the evidence collector will contaminate the evidence through perspiration.

c.   Care must be taken so as not to fold an article of clothing through a suspect seminal stain or to allow the stain to rub against the surface of the packaging material.

d.   Saliva is to be collected from the victim and suspect(s). The saliva can be dried on a clean paper towel.

e.   Have a physician or nurse collect a minimum of 7 cc. of blood from the victim and all suspects in a vacuum tube that doesn't contain either a preservative or an anti-coagulant. Also, collect a minimum of 7 cc. of blood containing the preservative EDTA. This blood will be used for DNA testing.

f.   Collect approximately 15-20 pulled pubic hairs and 50 full-length head hairs from both the victim and suspect(s).

g.   Label all evidence containers. The evidence collector's name or initials, the date, and the sampling locations are to be shown. All items collected are to be described in the evidence collector's field notes.

DNA—A New Forensic Science Tool

Learning Objectives

1. Learn the parts of a nucleotide and know how they are linked together to make DNA.
2. Understand how DNA strands coil into a double helix.
3. Describe the concept of base pairing as it relates to the double helix structure of DNA.
4. Explain how the sequence of bases along a DNA strand ultimately determines the structure of proteins that are synthesized within the body.
5. Describe how a double-strand DNA replicates itself. What are the implications of this process for forensic science?
6. Understand how DNA can be cut and spliced into a foreign DNA strand. Describe some commercial applications of this recombinant DNA technology.
7. Explain the difference between DNA strands which code for the production of proteins and those strands which contain repeating sequences of bases.
8. Explain what is meant by a restriction fragment length polymorphism (RFLP).
9. Describe the process of typing DNA by the RFLP technique and explain how DNA band patterns are interpreted.
10. Explain the technology of polymerase chain reaction (PCR) and how it's applied to forensic science.
11. Understand the difference between RFLP and PCR.
12. Explain the latest DNA typing technique, Short Tandem Repeat (STR) analysis.
13. Explain the difference beween nuclear DNA and mitochondrial DNA.
14. Discuss the application of a DNA computerized data-base to criminal investigation.
15. List the necessary procedures to be taken for the proper preservation of bloodstained evidence for laboratory DNA analysis.

General Comments

Students should be referred to the Internet Web site, "Simulation DQ-Alpha." This Web site generates a random DQ-Alpha (DQA1), (http://cqi-server.shadow.net/~mchinsee/scripts/simscrpt.pl), strip from a fictious DNA analysis. The user chooses which alleles he or she thinks are correct and can check their answer against the hypertexted result. This interactive Web site allows the user to learn how to read DQ-Alpha (DQA1) strips and test their interpretive abilities against the computer.

SUGGESTED EXPERIMENTS

Using a kit such as the one supplied by Lab-Aids Inc., 17 Colt Court, Ronkonkoma, N.Y. 11779, the student can build a model of DNA to see what a double helix structure looks like. The components are made of color-coded plastic and are easily assembled and disassembled. The model is flexible and is twisted to form the double helix structure. Lab-Aid kit no. 1271, "Forensic Science: Introduction to DNA Fingerprinting," simulates a crime scene and instructs students on how to interpret DNA X-ray films. Another Lab-Aids kit (no. 75) introduces students to the concept of PCR. Another interesting experiment is based on the Feulgen reaction where DNA in plant cells can be stained purple. With the aid of a microscope, students can view DNA in a plant cell. A DNA staining kit is available from Lab-Aids, Inc. (no. 170).

SUGGESTED EXAMINATION QUESTIONS

__d__   1.   Examples of polymers that contain repeating units known as nucleotides are:
  a. Hemoglobin
  b. Starch
  c. Cellulose
  d. DNA
  e. Paints

__b__   2.   How many different bases are associated with the makeup of DNA?
  a. 3
  b. 4
  c. 5
  d. 6
  e. None of the above

__d__   3.   Assume that two strands of DNA have been separated and that the base sequence on one strand is ATGC. State the sequence of bases on the second stand.
  a. GCAT
  b. ACTC
  c. TGGC
  d. TACG
  e. GACG

_b_   4. The production of amino acid is coded by a sequence of how
           many bases on the DNA molecule?
           a. 2
           b. 3
           c. 4
           d. 5
           e. 6

_c_   5. Portions of the DNA molecule useful for DNA typing:
           a. Code for the production of proteins.
           b. Are useful for recombinant DNA.
           c. Are repeated many times.
           d. Are useful for the production of insulin.
           e. Can determine if a person has sickle-cell anemia.

_e_   6. The following steps compose the DNA typing process: (1)
           electrophoresis, (2) Southern blotting, (3) hybridization with
           a radioactive probe, (4) digestion with restriction enzyme,
           (5) process with X-ray film. List these steps in their proper
           sequence.
           a. 1,2,3,4,5
           b. 2,1,3,4,5
           c. 4,5,1,2,3
           d. 5,4,3,2,1
           e. 4,1,2,3,5

_d_   7. The first commercial and validated PCR-based typing system
           for forensic science applications is:
           a. HLA
           b. A-B-O
           c. PGM
           d. DQA1
           e. p30

_c_   8. The concept of simultaneously extracting, amplifying, and
           detecting a combination of STRs is known as:
           a. PCR
           b. THO1
           c. Multiplexing
           d. Electrophoresis
           e. Polymarker

_c_   9. A nylon strip to which DNA probes have been attached
           forms the basis of the technology relating to:
           a. STR typing
           b. RFLP analysis
           c. DQA1 and Polymarker typing
           d. PGM typing
           e. STR and Polymarker typing

<u>e</u> 10. Which of the following statements about mitochondrial DNA is incorrect?
   a. Mitochondrial DNA is located outside the cell's nucleus.
   b. Mitochondrial DNA is constructed in a loop configuration.
   c. Two regions of mitochondrial DNA have been found to be highly variable in the human population.
   d. Many copies of mitochondrial DNA's hypervariable regions are made by PCR.
   e. The number of repeat segments found in the hypervariable regions are used to type mitochondrial DNA.

11. The victim of a homicide is wrapped in a blood-soaked sheet. Describe the proper steps to be taken in order to preserve the sheet for laboratory examination. List all necessary submissions that must be made for a thorough examination of blood evidence.
   A proper answer should include the following points.
   a. The sheet must be air dried out of the presence of direct sunlight or heat.
   b. The evidence collector must handle the sheet with a minimal amount of personal contact. All body fluids must be assumed to be infectious; hence, wearing disposable latex gloves while handling the evidence is required. Latex gloves will also significantly reduce the possibility that the evidence collector will contaminate the evidence through perspiration.
   c. The sheet is to be wrapped separately from other evidence. A paper bag or well-ventilated box is recommended. Refrigerate the container or store it in a cool location out of direct sunlight until delivery to the laboratory.
   d. From the victim and all suspects, have a physician or nurse collect a minimum of 7 cc. of blood in a vacuum tube that doesn't contain either a preservative or an anticoagulant. Also, collect a minimum of 7 cc. of blood containing the anticoagulant EDTA. This blood will be used for DNA testing.
   e. Label all evidence containers. The evidence collector's name or initials, the date, and the sampling locations are to be shown. All items collected are to be described in the evidence collector's field notes.

FINGERPRINTS

LEARNING OBJECTIVES

1. Name those individuals who have made significant contributions to the acceptance and development of fingerprint technology.
2. Define ridge characteristics.
3. Explain why a fingerprint is a permanent feature of the human anatomy.
4. List the three major fingerprint patterns and their respective subclasses.
5. Classify a set of fingerprints by the primary classification of the Henry system.
6. Explain what's meant by visible, plastic, and latent fingerprints.
7. List the techniques for developing latent fingerprints on non-porous objects.
8. Describe chemical techniques for developing prints on porous objects.
9. Describe the proper procedures for preserving a developed latent fingerprint.
10. Explain how a latent fingerprint image can be enhanced by digital imaging.

SUGGESTED EXPERIMENTS

Latent fingerprint development always proves to be a fun exercise. The following supplies can be purchased from police equipment suppliers such as, Sirchie, Youngsville, N.C.:

Brushes
Black and gray latent powder
Ninhydrin spray
Black and white hinge lifters
Transparent tape

Cyanoacrylate fuming can readily be demonstrated through the use of a small, hand-held fuming wand. This wand is available from Lightning Powder Co., Inc., Salem, Oregon.

SUGGESTED EXAMINATION QUESTIONS

__b__ 1. Which of the following types of fingerprints are more likely to be found impressed in soft wax?
   a. Visible
   b. Plastic
   c. Latent
   d. Hidden
   e. None of the above

 d   2. The first systematic system of individual classification and identification was introduced by:
   a. Francis Galton
   b. Richard Henry
   c. William Herschel
   d. Alphonse Bertillon
   e. None of the above

 a   3. The fingerprint pattern accounting for only five percent of all known patterns is the:
   a. Arch
   b. Radial loop
   c. Ulnar loop
   d. Whorl
   e. None of the above

 a   4. A fingerprint pattern having no delta is:
   a. Arch
   b. Loop
   c. Plain whorl
   d. Central pocket loop
   e. Accidental

 b   5. Protein residues are best developed into fingerprint impressions with:
   a. Iodine
   b. Ninhydrin
   c. Physical developer
   d. Dusting powder
   e. All of the above

 c   6. Which statement is true of a partial fingerprint?
   a. It must show at least a little of all ten fingers.
   b. Any print is sufficient for identification as long as there is enough to identify its basic pattern.
   c. Any print can identify a criminal if it shows an adequate number of ridge characteristics.
   d. At least 75% of the pattern must be present for identification.
   e. None of the above

 e   7. Which of the following is not a ridge characteristic of a fingerprint?
   a. Enclosure
   b. Bifurcation
   c. Island
   d. Ridge ending
   e. Core

b 8. Chemical methods for developing latent fingerprints must be used in the following sequence:
    a. Iodine, physical developer, ninhydrin
    b. Iodine, ninhydrin, physical developer
    c. Ninhydrin, iodine, physical developer
    d. Ninhydrin, physical developer, iodine
    e. Physical developer, ninhydrin, iodine

c 9. A chemical method used for developing prints on nonporous surfaces is:
    a. Physical developer
    b. Ninhydrin
    c. Applying the dye rhodamine 6G after fuming with cyanoacrylate
    d. DFO
    e. All of the above

FIREARMS, TOOL MARKS, AND OTHER IMPRESSIONS

CHAPTER

15

LEARNING OBJECTIVES

1. Describe techniques for rifling a barrel.
2. List the class and individual characteristics of bullets and cartridge cases.
3. Explain the utilization of the comparison microscope for the comparison of bullets and cartridge cases.
4. Distinguish caliber from gauge.
5. Explain the procedure for determining the distance from a target a weapon was fired.
6. Describe the laboratory tests utilized for determining whether an individual has fired a weapon. Emphasize the limitations of the present techniques.
7. Explain why it may be possible to restore an obliterated serial number.
8. List procedures for the proper collection and preservation of firearm evidence.
9. Explain how a suspect tool is compared to a tool mark.
10. Explain the forensic significance of class and individual characteristics to the comparison of impressions.
11. List some common field reagents used to enhance bloody footprints.

SUGGESTED EXPERIMENTS AND DEMONSTRATIONS

Students should be referred to the Internet Web site" An Introduction to Forensic Firearms Identification" [http://www.fire armsid.com]. This is a basic, informative Web site that provides an extensive collection of information relating to the identification of firearms. An individual can explore the details of how to examine bullets, cartridge cases, clothing for gunshot residues, and suspect shooters' hands for primer residues. Information on the latest technology involving automated firearm search systems Drugfire and IBIS can also be found within this site.

If a comparison microscope is available, a demonstration of bullet and cartridge casing comparisons is recommended.

The preparation of tool mark casts can readily be accomplished with liquid silicone rubber or silicone rubber putty (both available from Sirchie, Youngsville, N.C.).

I always require my class to prepare a cast of a footprint in the laboratory. Each student is requested to bring in a shoe box partially filled with soil. Other supplies required are: (1) An aerosol hair spray with a lacquer base (spraying the lacquer carefully over the impression will serve to harden it), (2) a 5-lb. bag of plaster of Paris, (3) tongue depressors or wire mesh to serve as reinforcing material, and (4) a mixing bowl.

The following guidelines should be followed when preparing the cast:

1. Spray the lacquer over the impression, being careful not to disturb the details of the impression.

2. The plaster of Paris is poured in two steps. First, add enough plaster to water to make an initial pouring approximately one-half-inch thick. The consistency of the mixture should be that of sour cream. The material should not be poured directly onto the impression, but over a tongue depressor or spoon to prevent marring the impression. The cast may then be reinforced with tongue depressors or wire mesh.

3. After reinforcing the cast, another mixture of plaster of Paris is prepared for an additional pouring approximately one-half-inch thick.

4. Before the plaster completely dries, it should be marked for identification on the upper surface.

SUGGESTED EXAMINATION QUESTIONS

<u>d</u> 1. Which of the following is not expected to show any evidential marks or impressions?
   a. A fired bullet
   b. A cartridge casing fired from a handgun
   c. A cartridge casing fired from a shotgun
   d. A shotgun pellet
   e. All of the above will show markings.

<u>c</u> 2. Which of the following procedures is not to be followed in collecting and packaging firearms evidence at the crime scene?
   a. Marking a fired bullet on its base for identification.
   b. Avoid inserting a stick or pencil into the barrel of a weapon.
   c. Marking an empty cartridge case on its base for identification.
   d. Unloading a weapon before shipping it to the crime laboratory.
   e. Making accurate measurements of exact locations where cartridge cases are found.

<u>b</u> 3. Two elements detected on the hands of an individual who has recently fired a weapon are:
   a. Zinc and copper
   b. Barium and antimony
   c. Barium and nitrates
   d. Antimony and iron
   e. Iron and lead

_c_ 4. Which of the following factors is least likely to be considered by the examining tool mark technician?
a. The direction of the tool movement as it passes over the surface
b. The side or portion of the tool making the impression
c. The brand name of the tool
d. The angle at which the tool was held
e. None of the above

_d_ 5. Which of the following results is not possible from a laboratory examination of firearm evidence?
a. Determining that two or more cartridge cases were fired from the same weapon
b. Determining how far from the victim the weapon was held
c. Restoring serial numbers ground off the gun
d. Identifying a bullet as having been combined with a particular shell prior to being discharged
e. All of the above can be determined from a laboratory examination of firearm evidence.

_b_ 6. Which of the following statements is true?
a. A bullet can be individualized to a weapon by the number and twist of its lands and grooves.
b. The comparison microscope is an indispensable tool of the firearm examiner.
c. The diameter of the bore of a rifled firearm is its gauge.
d. Carbonaceous smoke or soot deposited around a bullet hole is normally indicative of a discharge 12 to 18 feet or less from the target.
e. All of the above statements are true.

_d_ 7. A technique applicable for determining whether an individual has recently fired a weapon is:
a. Neutron activation analysis
b. Atomic absorption analysis
c. The scanning electron microscope
d. All of the above
e. None of the above

_a_ 8. The presence of gunpowder residues on a garment whose color conceals the existence of the residues is best revealed by:
a. Infrared photography
b. Ultraviolet photography
c. Color photography
d. Infrared spectrophotometry
e. Gas chromatography

DOCUMENT AND VOICE EXAMINATION

LEARNING OBJECTIVES

1. Define questioned document.
2. List some common individual characteristics associated with handwriting.
3. List some important guidelines to be followed for the collection of known writings for comparison to a questioned document.
4. Describe the precautions to be taken to minimize deception when a suspect is requested to write exemplars for comparison to a questioned document.
5. List some of the class and individual characteristics of a typewriter.
6. Describe the proper collection of typewritten exemplars.
7. List some of the techniques utilized by document examiners for uncovering alterations, erasures, obliterations, and variations in pen inks.
8. Describe the three parameters of speech that a voice print represents.

GENERAL COMMENTS

Students should be referred to the Internet Web site "Questioned Document Examination" [www.qdewill.com]. This a basic, informative web page that answers frequently asked questions concerning document examination, explains the application of typical document examinations, and details the basic facts and theory of handwriting and signatures. There are also noted document examination cases hypertexted to this web site for the user to read and recognize the real-life application of forensic document examination.

SUGGESTED EXAMINATION QUESTIONS

  _c_   1. Document examiners frequently uncover the original writing of words that have been crossed out with the aid of:
      a. Color photography
      b. Transmitted radiation
      c. Infrared radiation
      d. Side lighting
      e. Thin-layer chromatography

__d__ 2. When dictating to a person in order to obtain samples of handwriting, one should not:

  a. Use paper similar to that of the questioned document.

  b. Use a pen similar to that of the questioned document.

  c. Dictate the contents of the text at least three times.

  d. Allow the suspect to view the questioned document before dictating it.

  e. Use similar or the same letter and word grouping as used in the questioned document.

__e__ 3. If an investigator is to prepare standards from a suspect typewriter, the following procedure is recommended:

  a. Partial copies of the suspect text are to be typed in light, medium, and heavy touches.

  b. Prepare at least one copy of the text in full word-for-word order.

  c. Each character should be typed without the ribbon.

  d. Examine the type impressions left on the ribbon.

  e. All of the above are recommended procedures.

__a__ 4. Inks on handwritten documents may be compared for their chemical composition by the technique of:

  a. Thin-layer chromatography

  b. Infrared spectrophotometry

  c. Ultraviolet spectrophotometry

  d. Gas chromatography

  e. None of the above

__c__ 5. Which of the following statements is false?

  a. An inconclusive finding by a document examiner may be due to an insufficient number of known writings available for comparison.

  b. Any object that contains handwritten or typewritten markings whose source or authenticity is in doubt is a questioned document.

  c. Once adulthood is reached, an individual's handwriting generally will not change with age.

  d. In the case of *Gilbert* v. *California* the court held that the taking of handwriting exemplars was not prohibited by the fifth amendment.

  e. Writings on a charred document may be revealed by reflecting light off the paper's surface at different angles.

6. Illuminating a document with blue-green light and using infrared-sensitive paper to record the light emanating from the document's surface describes the technique of _____. (infrared luminescence)

_d_   7. A voice print portrays:
        a. The frequency of speech
        b. The time of speech
        c. The intensity of speech
        d. All of the above
        e. Choices a and b

Forensic Science on the Internet

Learning Objectives

1. Explain the Internet and how it is structured.
2. Introduce search engines along with the mechanisms used to search for information on the Internet.
3. Describe other types of information retrieval, such as mailing lists and news groups, available through the Internet.
4. Introduce the student to retrieving information about forensic science on the Internet.

General Comments

Students should be encouraged to become familiar with Reddy's Forensic Home Page (http://haven.ios.com/~nyrc/homepage.html) and Zeno's Forensic Page (http://forensic.to/forensic.html). These pages contain detailed listings of Web pages relevant to forensic science. Students should also be encouraged to explore the Police Officer's Internet Directory (http://www.officers.com). This directory encompasses many of the Web pages relevant to the criminal justice field and of interest to police officers.

Suggested Examination Questions

__d__ 1. The area of the Internet where all the documents of information are collected is the:
   a. Uniform resource locator
   b. Domain
   c. Mailing list
   d. Worldwide web
   e. Hypertext

__b__ 2. A quick method for switching back and forth between related web pages is to use:
   a. Search engines
   b. Hypertext
   c. Hypertext transfer protocol
   d. File transfer protocol
   e. Newsgroups

_e_   3. A(n) _____ is an automated search tool used to locate information on the Internet.
   a. Uniform resource locator
   b. Modem
   c. Mailing list
   d. Hypertext
   e. Search engine

_b_   4. If an individual wishes to send a message to another individual located in another part of the world, which system would they use?
   a. File transfer protocol
   b. Electronic mail
   c. Worldwide web
   d. Hypertext transfer protocol
   e. Newsgroups

_b_   5. A service offered through the Internet that will send messages concerning a specific topic directly to your e-mail account is:
   a. File transfer protocol
   b. Mailing list
   c. Newsgroups
   d. Worldwide web
   e. None of the above

_c_   6. Which service will allow the user to select informative messages of their choice from the system's bulletin board-like setup?
   a. Worldwide web
   b. Mailing list
   c. Newsgroups
   d. Electronic mail
   e. None of the above

_a_   7. A _____ will provide the user with the capabilities for accessing web pages on the worldwide web.
   a. Browser
   b. Hypertext Transfer Protocol
   c. Uniform Resource Locator
   d. Modem
   e. None of the above

Answers to Chapter Review Questions

Chapter 1

2. Sherlock Holmes
4. Francis Galton
6. Calvin Goddard
8. Hans Gross
10. Los Angeles
12. regional
14. FBI; Drug Enforcement Administration; Bureau of Alcohol; Tobacco and Firearms; and U.S.Postal Service
16. physical evidence
18. firearms
20. evidence collection
22. *Daubert* v. *Merrell Dow Pharmaceutical*
24. *Coppolino* v. *State*
26. True
28. training
30. true

Chapter 2

2. False
4. excluded
6. unaltered
8. rough
10. carriers
12. is not
14. False
16. air-dried
18. chain of custody
20. warrantless

Chapter 3

2. exclude
4. probability
6. class
8. corroboration
10. False
12. natural variations

Chapter 4

2. chemical
4. metric, gram, liter
6. 1/1000
8. milliliter
10. 453.6 grams
12. Temperature
14. 100
16. equal-arm balance
18. float
20. refractive index
22. amorphous
24. dispersion
26. individual
28. flotation
30. frequency of occurrence
32. narrower
34. False
36. False
38. density-gradient

CHAPTER 5

2. elements
4. periodic
6. compounds
8. solid
10. sublimation
12. phases
14. Inorganic
16. spectrophotometry
18. True
20. True
22. retention time

24. room
26. visualized
28. False
30. True
32. False
34. lower
36. photons
38. less
40. Beer's
42. monochromator
44. mass spectrometry

CHAPTER 6

2. ten
4. absorb, emit
6. True
8. is
10. emission spectrograph
12. atomic absorption spectroscopy
14. False
16. are not

18. is
20. atomic number
22. True
24. atomic mass number
26. False
28. electrons
30. neutrons
32. diffraction pattern

CHAPTER 7

2. virtual
4. objective lens
6. virtual
8. transmitted
10. condenser
12. binocular
14. 200x
16. field of view

18. depth of focus
20. comparison
22. stereoscopic
24. working distance
26. perpendicular
28. birefringent
30. scanning electron

CHAPTER 8

2. cuticle, cortex, medulla
4. cortex
6. medullary index
8. absent
10. anagen, catagen, telogen
12. comparison
14. is
16. often
18. anagen
20. 24
22. cotton

24. synthetic fibers
26. Polymers
28. Proteins
30. visible
32. birefringence
34. class
36. layer structure
38. electrocoat primer
40. binder
42. True

CHAPTER 9

2. high
4. True
6. regular
8. Opium
10. heroin
12. hallucinogens
14. tetrahydrocannabinol (THC)
16. liquid hashish
18. clandestine
20. Barbiturates
22. Methaqualone (Quaalude)
24. False

26. intravenous
28. Cocaine
30. False
32. Controlled Substances Act
34. one
36. False
38. Marquis
40. Scott
42. chromatography
44. mass spectrometry
46. chain of custody

CHAPTER 10

2. False
4. True
6. 30, 90
8. oxidation, excretion
10. liver
12. 0.015
14. artery, vein
16. alveoli
18. lower
20. absorption
22. gas chromatography

24. False
26. nonalcoholic
28. 0.10
30. morphine
32. acids, bases
34. acidic
36. immunoassay
38. carbon monoxide
40. False
42. poor
44. Drug Recognition Expert

CHAPTER 11

2. oxidation
4. Energy
6. breaking, formation
8. liberate
10. heat of combustion
12. True
14. gaseous
16. Pyrolysis
18. increases
20. oxygen
22. True
24. True
26. Airtight
28. pattern

30. could have
32. explosion
34. High
36. confined
38. initiating, noninitiating
40. True
42. PETN
44. crater
46. microscopic
48. color tests, thin-layer chromatography, high-performance liquid chromatography
50. X-ray diffraction

CHAPTER 12

2. True
4. serum
6. antigens
8. neither
10. Rh
12. only a specific
14. B,A
16. antibodies
18. be
20. O
22. 42
24. All
26. Luminol

28. can
30. 80
32. polymorphic
34. True
36. chromosomes
38. father
40. homozygous
42. genotype
44. BB, BO
46. A, B, AB
48. spermatozoa
50. p30
52. True

CHAPTER 13

2. DNA
4. nucleotide
6. four
8. T,C
10. proteins
12. Three
14. True
16. False
18. lengths
20. Southern

22. ATC
24. True
26. Short tandem repeats (STRs)
28. capillary electrophoresis
30. mother
32. Two
34. thirteen
36. False
38. two

CHAPTER 14

2. Anthropometry
4. True
6. ridge characteristics
8. dermal papillae
10. cannot
12. loop
14. radial
16. delta
18. core
20. plain arch
22. whorl

24. cannot
26. visible fingerprint
28. latent fingerprints
30. chemical
32. ninhydrin
34. False
36. Fluorescence
38. photography
40. Frequency Fourier
    Transform Analysis

CHAPTER 15

2. caliber
4. individual
6. False
8. smooth
10. False
12. True
14. False
16. infrared

18. yard
20. barium, antimony
22. True
24. base, nose
26. gunpowder residue
28. striations
30. photography, casting

CHAPTER 16

2. likely
4. False
6. less
8. conscious

10. infrared, ultraviolet
12. infrared
14. thin-layer
16. voice print

CHAPTER 17

2. modem
4. URL
6. search engine

LIST OF TRANSPARENCY MASTERS

T-1   Figure 1-4
       Typical blowfly cycle

T-2   Figure 2-3
       Diagram of a Crime Scene

T-3   Figure 2-4
       Examples of crime-scene search patterns

T-4   Figure 3-4
       Determining the Path of a Bullet

T-5   Figure 4-1
       Metric volume

T-6   Figure 4-3
       Celsius and Fahrenheit temperature scales

T-7   Figure 4-4
       The measurement of mass

T-8   Figure 4-7
       The bending of light rays

T-9   Figure 4-8
       Diagram of sodium chloride crystal

T-10   Figure 4-9
       Dispersion of light by a prism

T-11   Figure 4-18
       Production of radial and concentric fractures in glass

T-12   Figure 4-20
       Two bullet holes in glass

T-13   Figure 5-1
       The periodic table

T-14   Figure 5-4
       The chromatography process

T-15   Figure 5-5
       The basic gas chromatograph

T-16   Figure 5-6
       Identification of barbiturates by gas chromatography

T-17   Figure 5-7
       Pyrogram of an automotive paint

T-18   Figure 5-8
       Thin-layer chromatography

T-19   Figure 5-12
       The frequency of the lower wave is twice that of the upper wave.

T-20   Figure 5-15
       Parts of a Simple Spectrophotometer

T-21   Figure 5-16
       Ultraviolet spectrum of heroin

T-22   Figure 5-18
       How GC-MS works

T-23   Figure 5-19
       (a) Mass spectrum of heroin and (b) Mass spectrum of cocaine

T-24   Figure 5-20 (b)
         The parts of a GC-MS

T-25   Figure 6-2
         A simple emission spectrograph

T-26   Figure 6-5
         Atomic structure of hydrogen and helium

T-27   Figure 6-6
         The absorption and emission of light by an atom

T-28   Figure 6-9
         X-ray diffraction

T-29   Figure 7-2
         The principle of the compound microscope

T-30   Figure 8-1
         The structure of hair

T-31   Figure 8-10
         Starch and cellulose polymers

T-32   Figure 8-19
         Pyrograms of automotive paints

T-33   Figure 10-4(b)
         The Breathalyzer

T-34   Figure 10-6
         An infrared breath-testing device

T-35   Figure 10-10
         Driving risk vs. blood alcohol concentration

T-36   Figure 10-11
         Blood alcohol level after drinking

T-37   Figure 10-13
         Gas chromatography/mass-spectrometry

T-38   Figure 11-5
         Gas chromatograph of gasoline before and after a fire

T-39   Figure 11-6
         Accelerant recovery by vapor concentration

T-40   Figure 11-7
         Utilization of GC-MS in fire investigation

T-41   Figure 12-1
         B antibodies will only cause cells with B antigens to agglutinate.

T-42   Figure 12-3
         Stimulating an animal to produce drug antibodies

T-43   Figure 12-5
         The precipitin test

T-44   Figure 12-6
         Cross-over electrophoresis

T-45   Figure 12-13
         Bloodstain Convergence

T-46   Figure 12-16
         Detection of p30 in semen by cross-over electrophoresis

T-47   Figure 13-1
         Nucleotides linked together to form a DNA strand

T-48   Figure 13-2
        The DNA helix

T-49   Figure 13-3
        Normal and sickle-cell hemoglobin

T-50   Figure 13-4
        Replication of DNA

T-51   Figure 13-6
        Recombinant DNA

T-52   Figure 13-7
        DNA segments containing repeating sequences of bases

T-53   Figure 13-8
        The DNA typing process

T-54   Figure 13-11
        PCR Process for DNA Typing

T-55   Figure 13-12
        THO1 Variants

T-56   Figure 13-13
        STR Multiplex System

T-57   Figure 13-14
        Separation of DNA segments by capillary electrophoresis

T-58   Figure 13-16
        Mitochondrial DNA

T-59   Figure 14-1
        Ridge characteristics

T-60   Figure 14-2
        Matching fingerprint ridge characteristics

T-61   Figure 14-5
        Loop patterns

T-62   Figure 14-6
        Whorl patterns

T-63   Figure 14-7
        Arch patterns

T-64   Figure 14-11
        Latent fingerprint detection with the aid of a laser

T-65   Figure 15-1
        Internal View of a Gun Barrel

T-66   Figure 15-10
        Parts of the IBIS System

Lab Manual

T-67   Figure 4-1
        The compound microscope

T-68   Figure 11-1
        Fingerprint patterns

T-69   Figure 11-2
        Fingerprint ridge characteristics

T-70   Figure 17-2
        Hair scale patterns

T-1 Typical Blowfly Cycle (Figure 1-4)

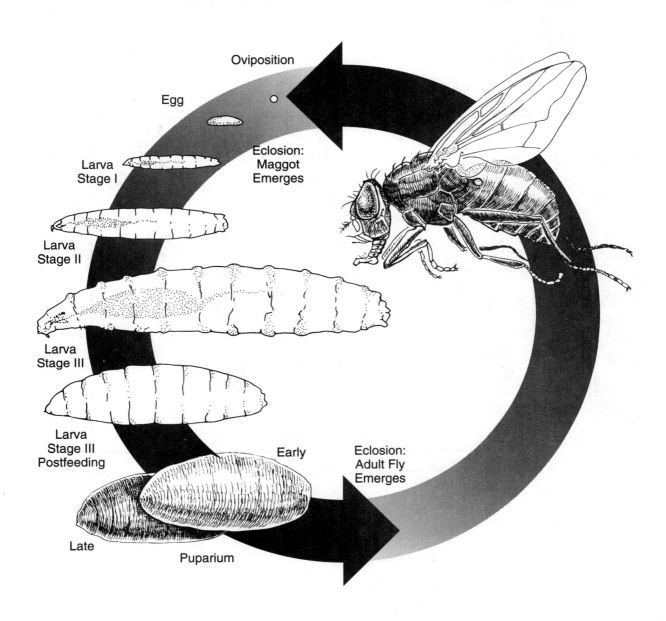

T-2 Diagram of a Crime Scene (Figure 2-3)

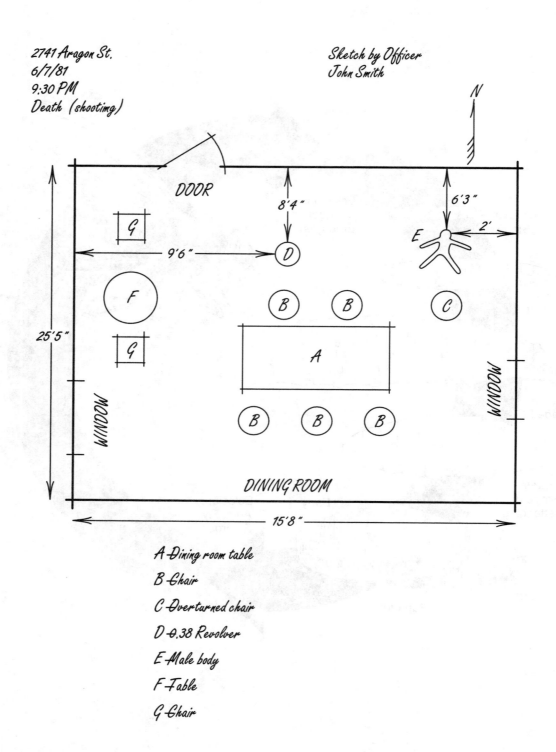

2741 Aragon St.
6/7/81
9:30 PM
Death (shooting)

Sketch by Officer
John Smith

N

DOOR

8'4"

6'3"

G

9'6"

D

E

2'

F

B

B

C

25'5"

A

WINDOW

WINDOW

G

B

B

B

DINING ROOM

15'8"

A Dining room table

B Chair

C Overturned chair

D 0.38 Revolver

E Male body

F Table

G Chair

T-3 Examples of Crime-Scene Seach Patterns (Figure 2-4)

Spiral search method

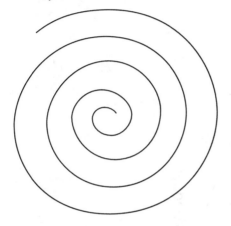

Grid method

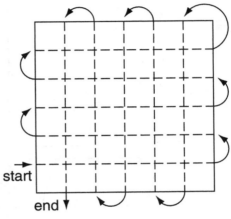

Strip or line search

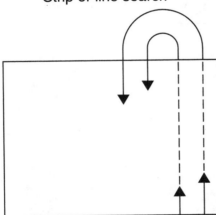

Quadrant or zone search

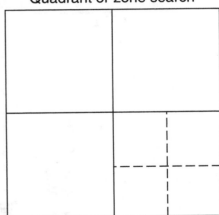

T-4 Determining the Path of a Bullet (Figure 3-4)

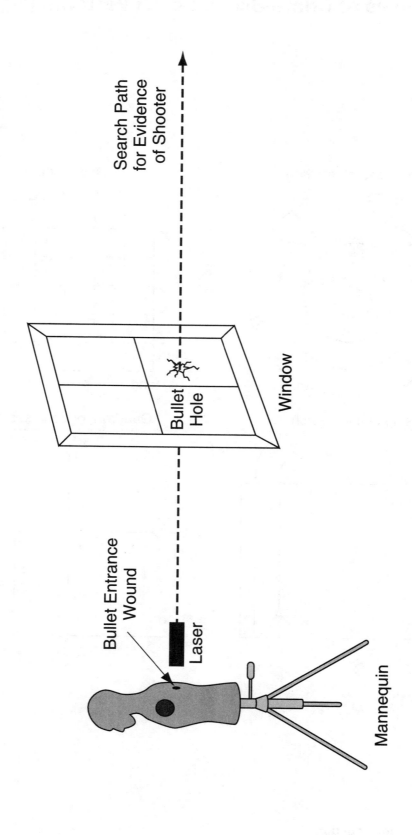

Search Path for Evidence of Shooter

Window

Bullet Hole

Bullet Entrance Wound

Laser

Mannequin

Criminalistics: An Introduction
to Forensic Science, 7/E
Saferstein

T-5 Metric Volume (Figure 4-1)

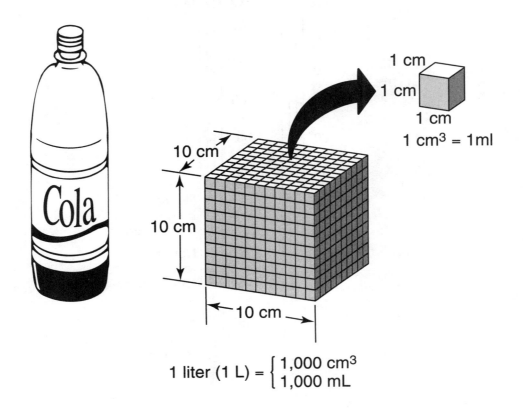

$$1 \text{ cm}^3 = 1 \text{ml}$$

$$1 \text{ liter (1 L)} = \begin{cases} 1{,}000 \text{ cm}^3 \\ 1{,}000 \text{ mL} \end{cases}$$

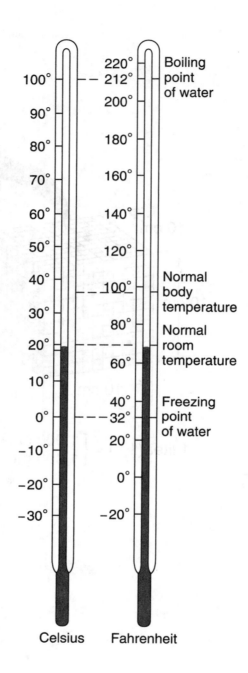

**Criminalistics: An Introduction
to Forensic Science, 7/E
Saferstein**

**© 2001 by Prentice-Hall, Inc.
Upper Saddle River, New Jersey 07458**

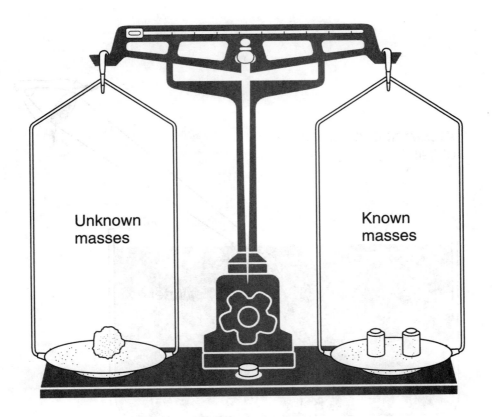

**Criminalistics: An Introduction
to Forensic Science, 7/E
Saferstein**

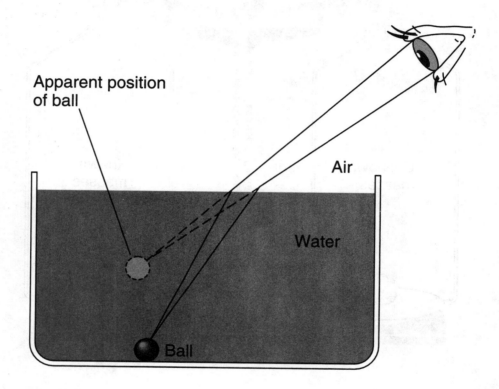

Apparent position
of ball

Air

Water

Ball

**Criminalistics: An Introduction
to Forensic Science, 7/E
Saferstein**

**© 2001 by Prentice-Hall, Inc.
Upper Saddle River, New Jersey 07458**

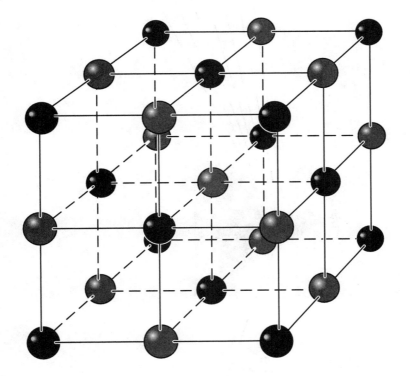

**Criminalistics: An Introduction
to Forensic Science, 7/E
Saferstein**

T-10   Dispersion of Light by a Prism (Figure 4-9)

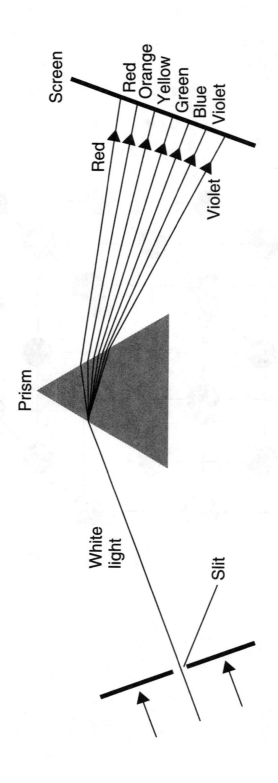

Criminalistics: An Introduction
to Forensic Science, 7/E
Saferstein

T-11   Production of Radial and Concentric Fractures in Glass (Figure 4-18)

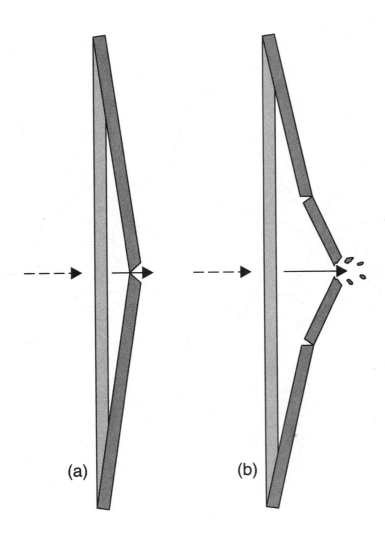

(a)   (b)

T-12 Two Bullet Holes in Glass (Figure 4-20)

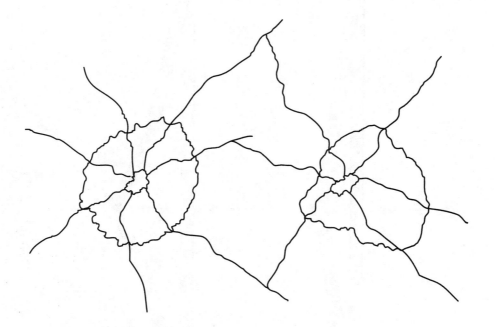

**Criminalistics: An Introduction
to Forensic Science, 7/E
Saferstein**

T-13 The Periodic Table (Figure 5-1)

Group	IA	IIA	IIIB	IVB	VB	VIB	VIIB	VIII			IB	IIB	IIIA	IVA	VA	VIA	VIIA	O
Period																		
1	1 H																	2 He
2	3 Li	4 Be											5 B	6 C	7 N	8 O	9 F	10 Ne
3	11 Na	12 Mg											13 Al	14 Si	15 P	16 S	17 Cl	18 Ar
4	19 K	20 Ca	21 Sc	22 Ti	23 V	24 Cr	25 Mn	26 Fe	27 Co	28 Ni	29 Cu	30 Zn	31 Ga	32 Ge	33 As	34 Se	35 Br	36 Kr
5	37 Rb	38 Sr	39 Y	40 Zr	41 Nb	42 Mo	43 Tc	44 Ru	45 Rh	46 Pd	47 Ag	48 Cd	49 In	50 Sn	51 Sb	52 Te	53 I	54 Xe
6	55 Cs	56 Ba	57 La (a)	72 Hf	73 Ta	74 W	75 Re	76 Os	77 Ir	78 Pt	79 Au	80 Hg	81 Tl	82 Pb	83 Bi	84 Po	85 At	86 Rn
7	87 Fr	88 Ra	89 Ac (b)	104 Unq	105 Unp	106 Unh	107 Uns	108 Uno	109 Une	110 Uun								

(a) Lanthanide Series

58 Ce	59 Pr	60 Nd	61 Pm	62 Sm	63 Eu	64 Gd	65 Tb	66 Dy	67 Ho	68 Er	69 Tm	70 Yb	71 Lu

(b) Actinide Series

90 Th	91 Pa	92 U	93 Np	94 Pu	95 Am	96 Cm	97 Bk	98 Cf	99 Es	100 Fm	101 Md	102 No	103 Lr

Criminalistics: An Introduction
to Forensic Science, 7/E
Saferstein

© 2001 by Prentice-Hall, Inc.
Upper Saddle River, New Jersey 07458

T-14 The Chromatography Process (Figure 5-4)

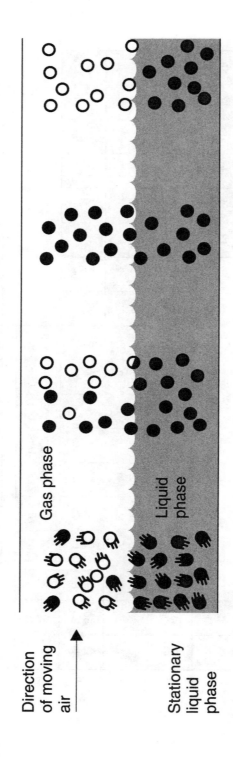

Direction
of moving
air

Gas phase

Liquid
phase

Stationary
liquid
phase

Criminalistics: An Introduction
to Forensic Science, 7/E
Saferstein

T-15 The Basic Gas Chromatograph (Figure 5-5)

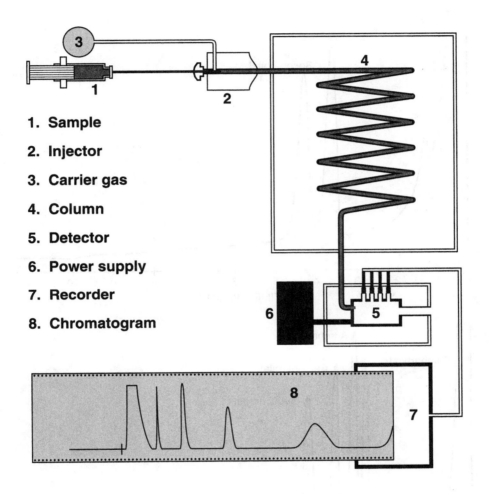

1. **Sample**
2. **Injector**
3. **Carrier gas**
4. **Column**
5. **Detector**
6. **Power supply**
7. **Recorder**
8. **Chromatogram**

**Criminalistics: An Introduction
to Forensic Science, 7/E
Saferstein**

T-16 Identification of Barbiturates by Gas Chromatography (Figure 5-6)

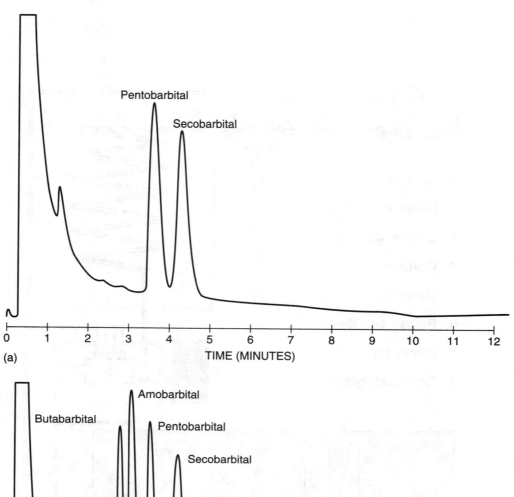

(a)

TIME (MINUTES)

Pentobarbital

Secobarbital

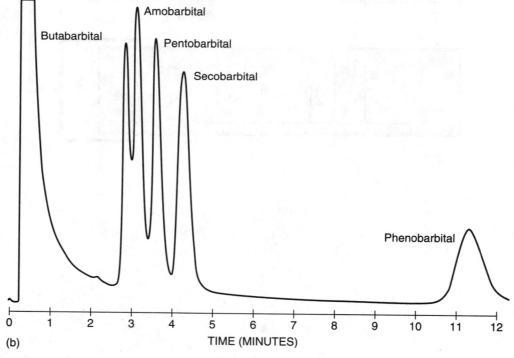

(b)

TIME (MINUTES)

Butabarbital

Amobarbital

Pentobarbital

Secobarbital

Phenobarbital

Criminalistics: An Introduction to Forensic Science, 7/E Saferstein

© 2001 by Prentice-Hall, Inc.
Upper Saddle River, New Jersey 07458

T-17   Pyrogram of an Automotive Paint (Figure 5-7)

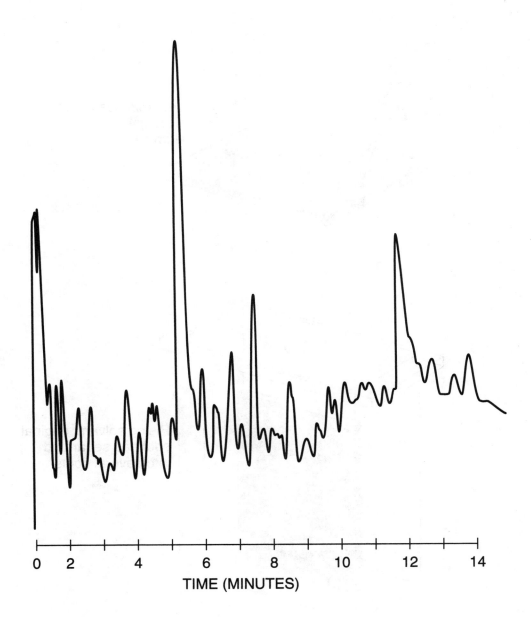

TIME (MINUTES)

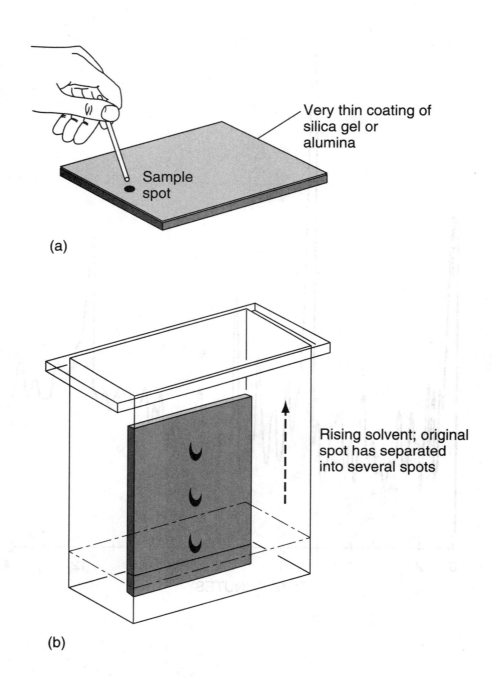

Very thin coating of silica gel or alumina

Sample spot

(a)

Rising solvent; original spot has separated into several spots

(b)

T-19 The Frequency of the Lower Wave Is Twice That of the Upper Wave (Figure 5-12)

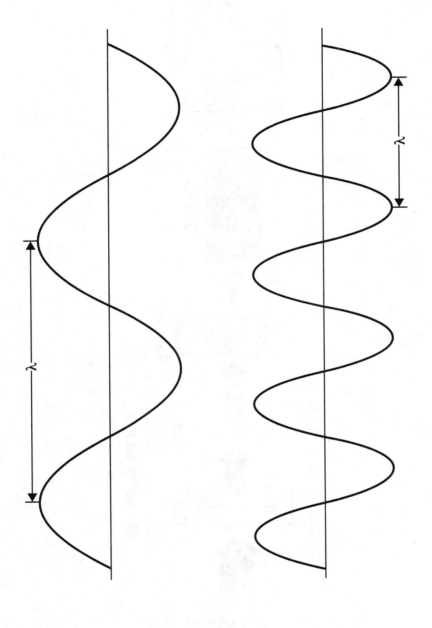

Criminalistics: An Introduction
to Forensic Science, 7/E
Saferstein

T-20 Parts of a Simple Spectrophotometer (Figure 5-15)

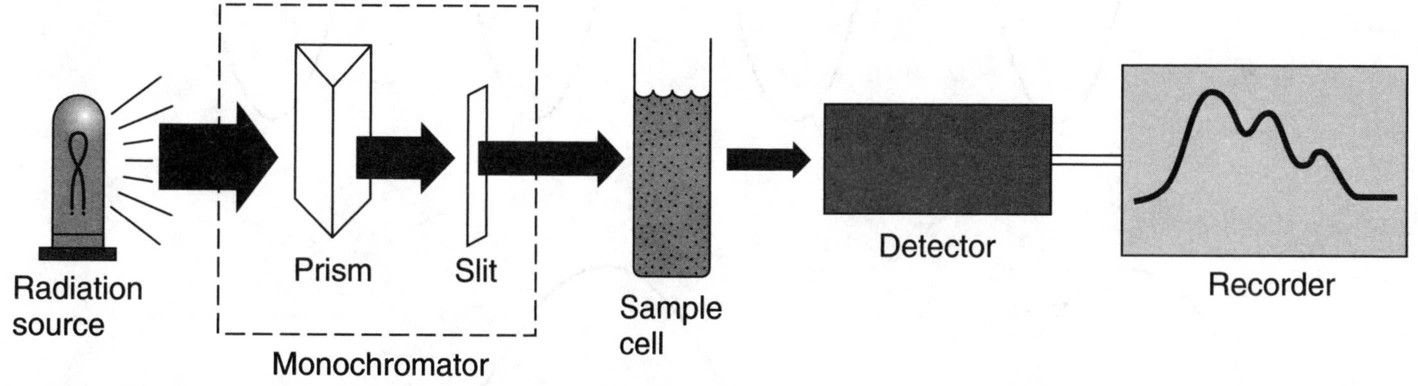

Radiation source

Monochromator
Prism
Slit

Sample cell

Detector

Recorder

Criminalistics: An Introduction
to Forensic Science, 7/E
Saferstein

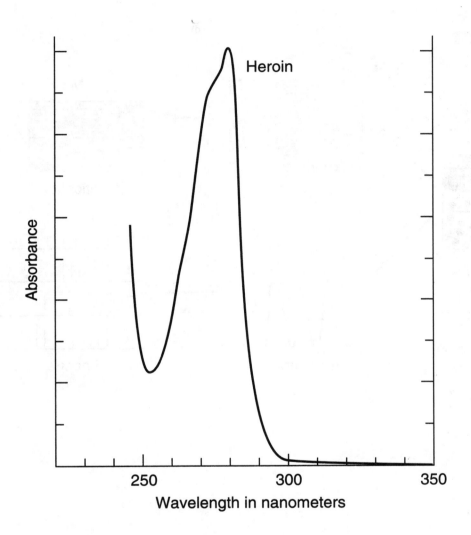

**Criminalistics: An Introduction
to Forensic Science, 7/E
Saferstein**

© 2001 by Prentice-Hall, Inc.
Upper Saddle River, New Jersey 07458

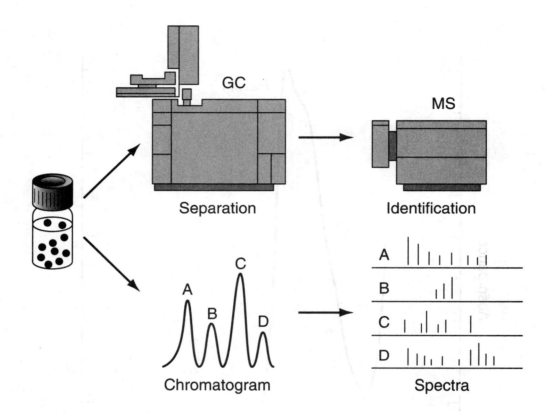

GC

MS

Separation

Identification

A

B

C

D

Chromatogram

Spectra

**Criminalistics: An Introduction
to Forensic Science, 7/E
Saferstein**

T-23 **(a) Mass Spectrum of Heroin and (b) Mass Spectrum of Cocaine (Figure 5-19)**

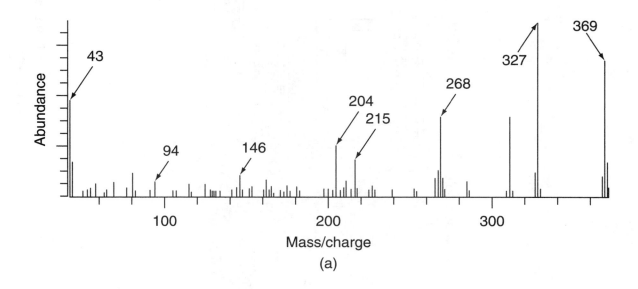

(a)

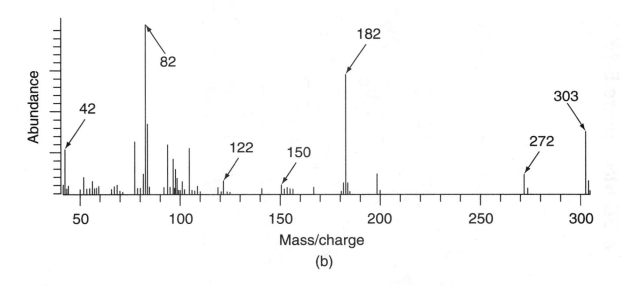

(b)

Criminalistics: An Introduction
to Forensic Science, 7/E
Saferstein

© 2001 by Prentice-Hall, Inc.
Upper Saddle River, New Jersey 07458

T-24 The Parts of a GC-MS (Figure 5-20b)

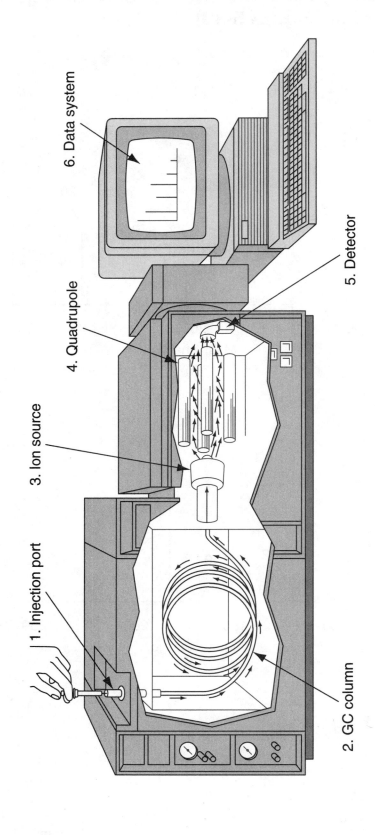

1. Injection port
2. GC column
3. Ion source
4. Quadrupole
5. Detector
6. Data system

Criminalistics: An Introduction
to Forensic Science, 7/E
Saferstein

T-25   A Simple Emission Spectrograph (Figure 6-2)

Photographic plate

Prism

Lens

Sample between carbon electrodes

Criminalistics: An Introduction to Forensic Science, 7/E
Saferstein

T-26 Atomic Structure of Hydrogen and Helium (Figure 6-5)

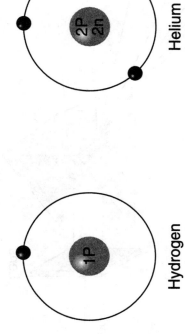

Helium

Hydrogen

Criminalistics: An Introduction
to Forensic Science, 7/E
Saferstein

T-27 The Absorption and Emission of Light by an Atom (Figure 6-6)

(a)

(b)

Criminalistics: An Introduction
to Forensic Science, 7/E
Saferstein

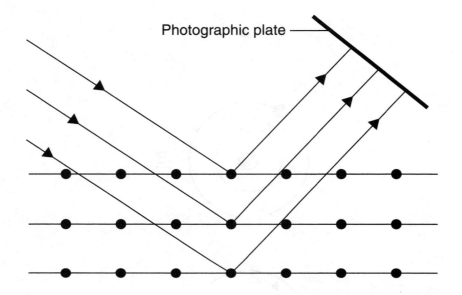

Photographic plate

T-29 The Principle of the Compound Microscope
(Figure 7-2)

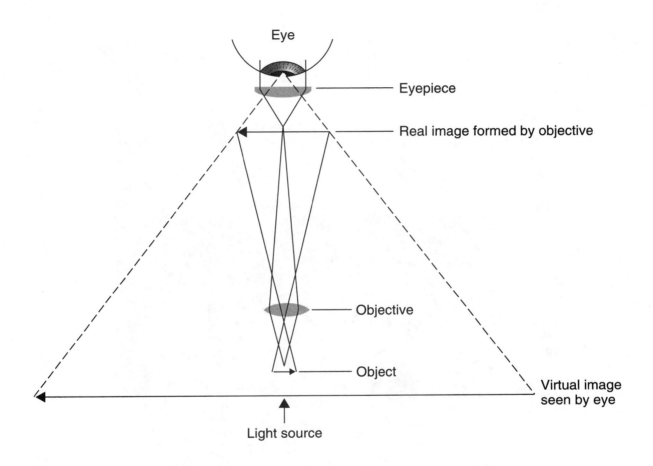

Eye

Eyepiece

Real image formed by objective

Objective

Object

Virtual image seen by eye

Light source

Criminalistics: An Introduction to Forensic Science, 7/E Saferstein

© **2001 by Prentice-Hall, Inc. Upper Saddle River, New Jersey 07458**

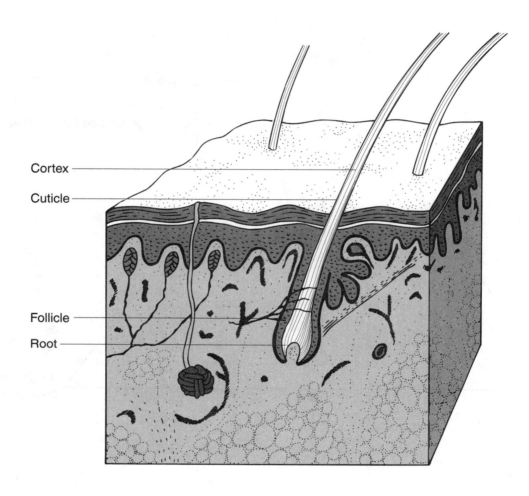

Cortex

Cuticle

Follicle

Root

**Criminalistics: An Introduction
to Forensic Science, 7/E
Saferstein**

T-31 Starch and Cellulose Polymers (Figure 8-10)

Starch

Cellulose

© 2001 by Prentice-Hall, Inc.
Upper Saddle River, New Jersey 07458

Criminalistics: An Introduction
to Forensic Science, 7/E
Saferstein

T-32 Pyrograms of Automotive Paints (Figure 8-19)

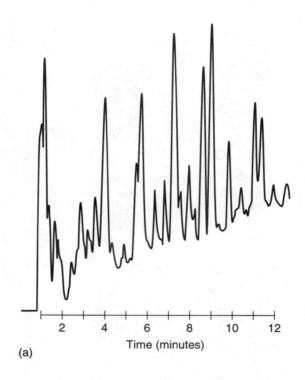

(a)

Time (minutes)

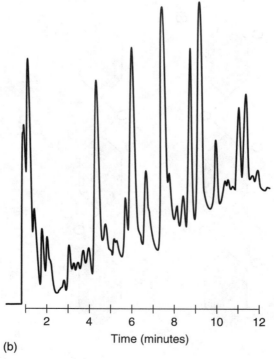

(b)

Time (minutes)

T-33 The Breathalyzer (Figure 10-4b)

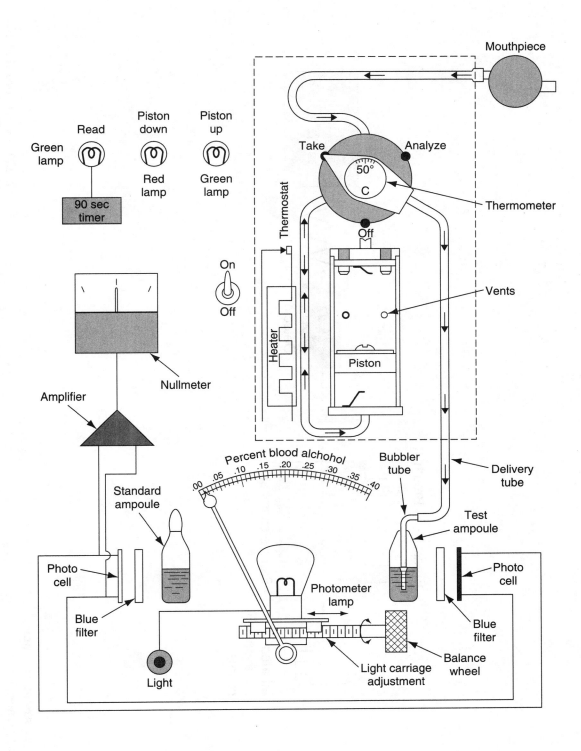

Criminalistics: An Introduction to Forensic Science, 7/E Saferstein

T-34   An Infrared Breath-Testing Device (Figure 10-6)

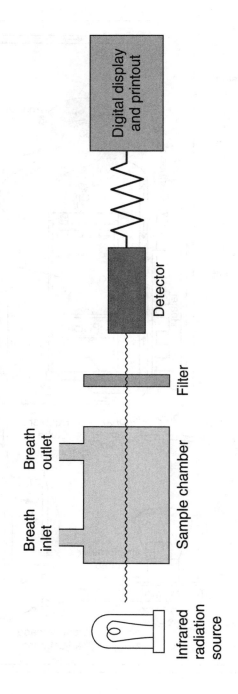

Criminalistics: An Introduction
to Forensic Science, 7/E
Saferstein

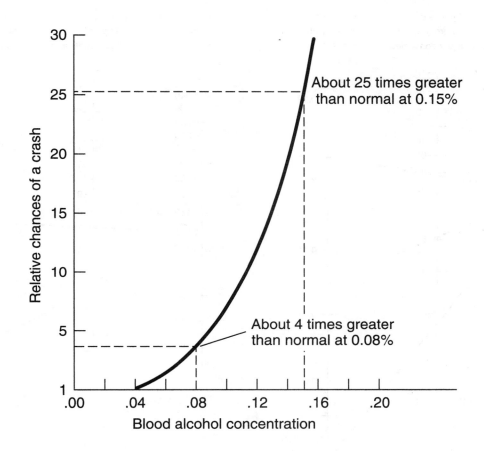

T-36   Blood Alcohol Level after Drinking (Figure 10-11)

How to Tell What Your Blood Alcohol Level Is After Drinking

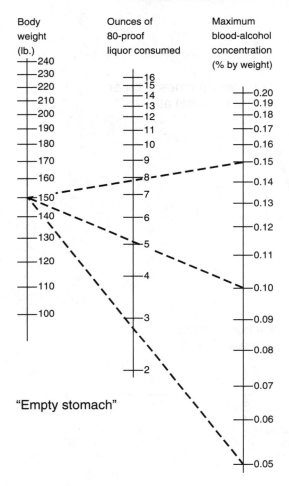

"Empty stomach"

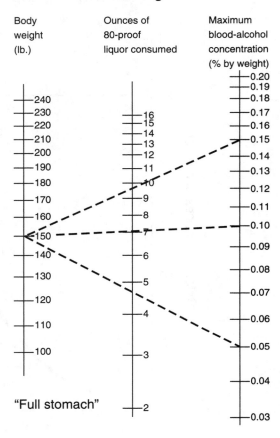

"Full stomach"

**Criminalistics: An Introduction
to Forensic Science, 7/E
Saferstein**

**© 2001 by Prentice-Hall, Inc.
Upper Saddle River, New Jersey 07458**

T-37 Gas Chromatography/Mass-Spectrometry (Figure 10-13)

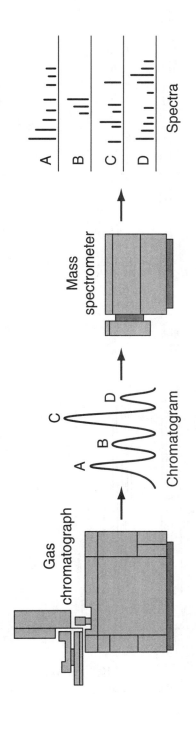

Criminalistics: An Introduction
to Forensic Science, 7/E
Saferstein

T-38 Gas Chromatograph of Gasoline Before and After a Fire (Figure 11-5)

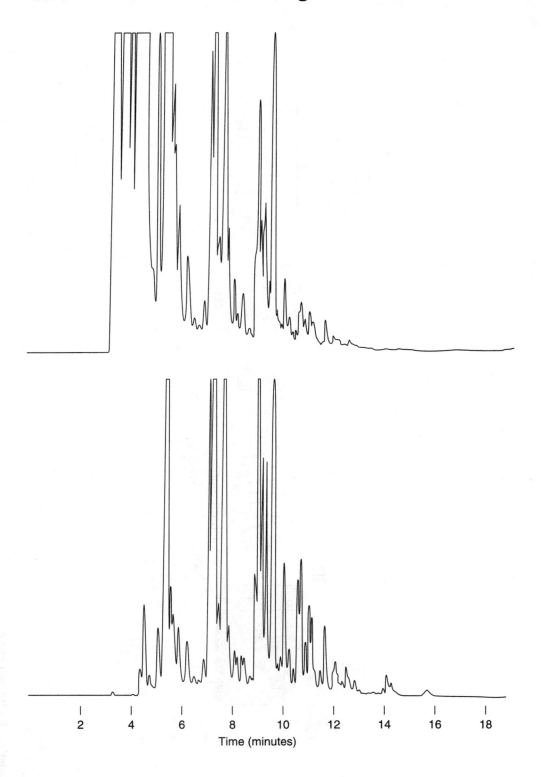

Time (minutes)

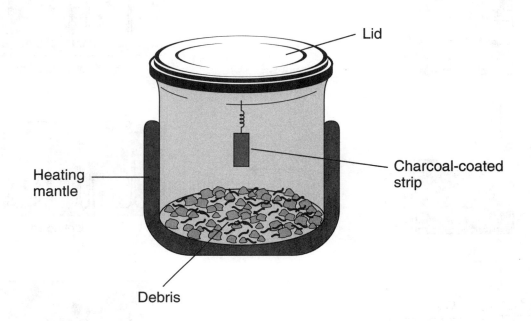

Lid

Charcoal-coated strip

Heating mantle

Debris

T-40 Utilization of GC-MS in Fire Investigation (Figure 11-7)

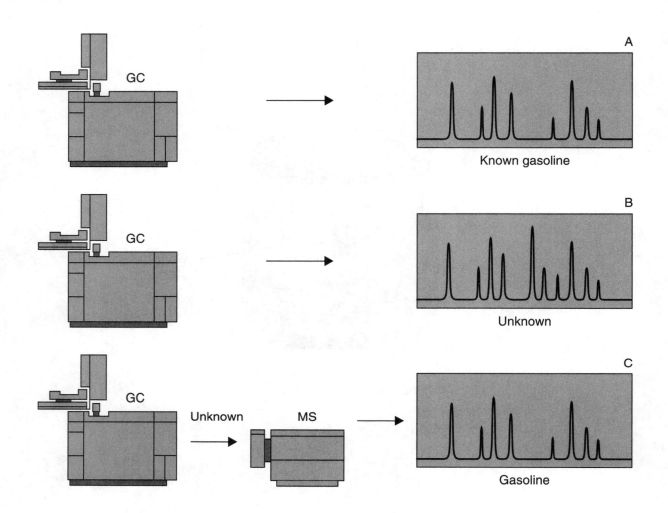

GC → Known gasoline **A**

GC → Unknown **B**

GC → Unknown → MS → Gasoline **C**

Criminalistics: An Introduction
to Forensic Science, 7/E
Saferstein

T-41 B Antibodies Will Only Case Cells with B Antigens to Agglutinate (Figure 12-1)

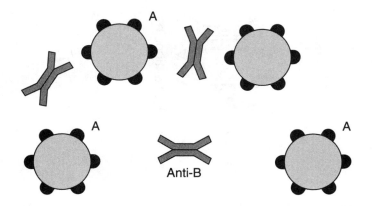

Anti-B

Red blood cells containing A antigens
will not combine with B antibodies

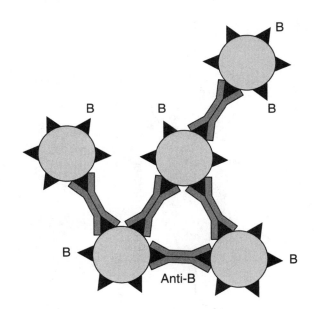

Anti-B

Red blood cells containing B antigens
are agglutinated or clumped together
in the presence of B antibodies

**Criminalistics: An Introduction
to Forensic Science, 7/E
Saferstein**

© 2001 by Prentice-Hall, Inc.
Upper Saddle River, New Jersey 07458

T-42 Stimulating an Animal to Produce Drug Antibodies (Figure 12-3)

Drug

Protein carrier

Drug antibodies

Criminalistics: An Introduction
to Forensic Science, 7/E
Saferstein

T-43   The Precipitin Test (Figure 12-5)

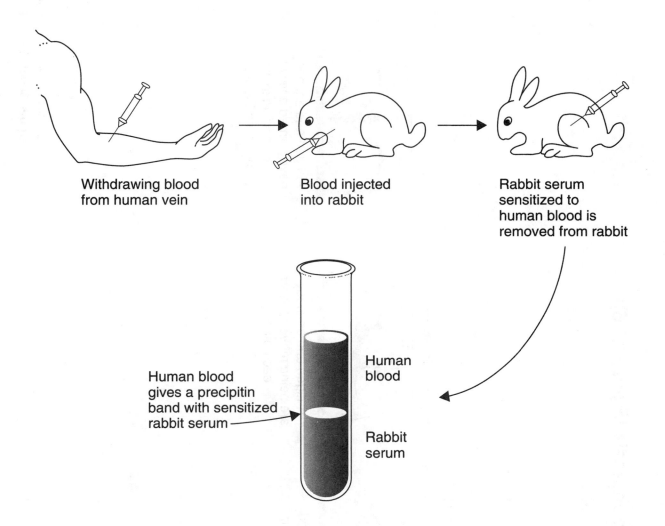

Withdrawing blood
from human vein

Blood injected
into rabbit

Rabbit serum
sensitized to
human blood is
removed from rabbit

Human blood
gives a precipitin
band with sensitized
rabbit serum

Human
blood

Rabbit
serum

**Criminalistics: An Introduction
to Forensic Science, 7/E
Saferstein**

**© 2001 by Prentice-Hall, Inc.
Upper Saddle River, New Jersey 07458**

T-44 Cross-Over Electrophoresis (Figure 12-6)

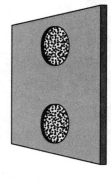

Antigen and antibody are added to their respective wells

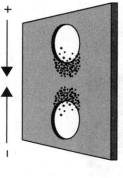

Antigen and antibody are being moved toward each other

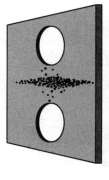

Antigen and antibody have formed a visible precipitin line in the gel between the wells

Criminalistics: An Introduction
to Forensic Science, 7/E
Saferstein

T-45   Bloodstain Convergence (Figure 12-13)

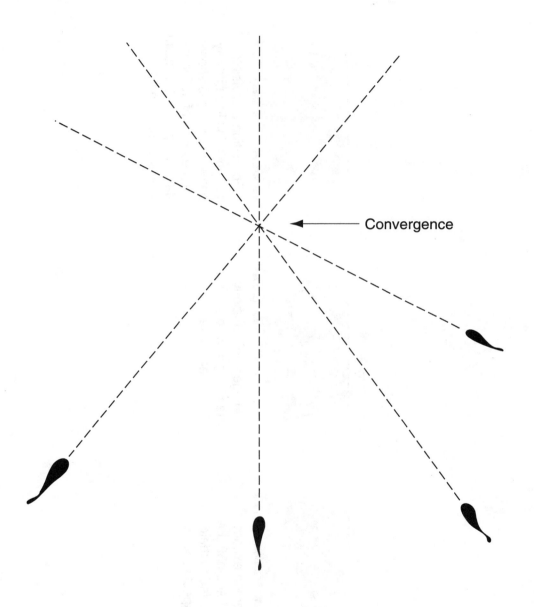

Convergence

**Criminalistics: An Introduction
to Forensic Science, 7/E
Saferstein**

T-46   Detection of p30 in Semen by Cross-Over Electrophoresis (Figure 12-16)

Semen extract and anti-p30 are added to their respective wells

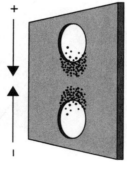

Antigen and antibody are being moved toward each other

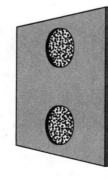

Formation of a visible precipitation line midway between the wells shows the presence of p30 in the stain and proves the stain is seminal in nature

© 2001 by Prentice-Hall, Inc.
Upper Saddle River, New Jersey 07458

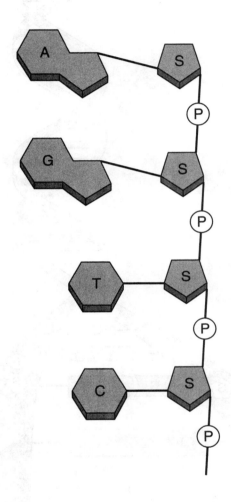

**Criminalistics: An Introduction
to Forensic Science, 7/E
Saferstein**

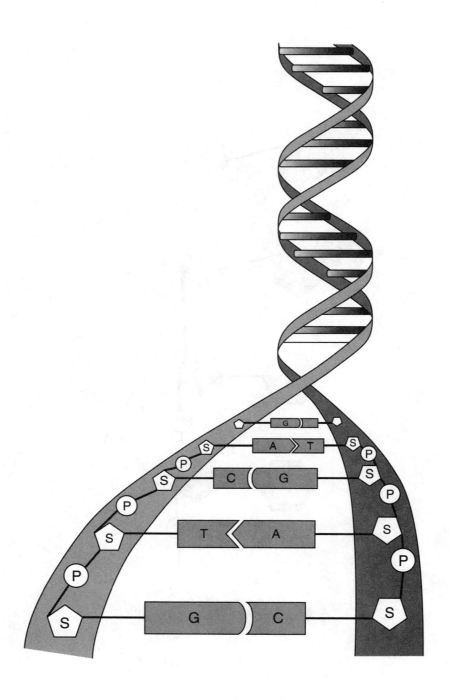

**Criminalistics: An Introduction
to Forensic Science, 7/E
Saferstein**

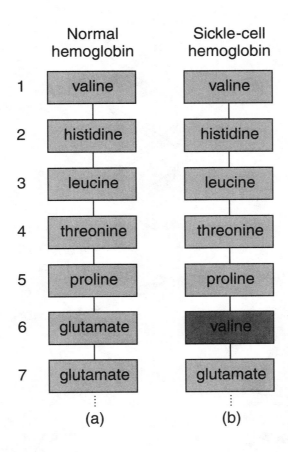

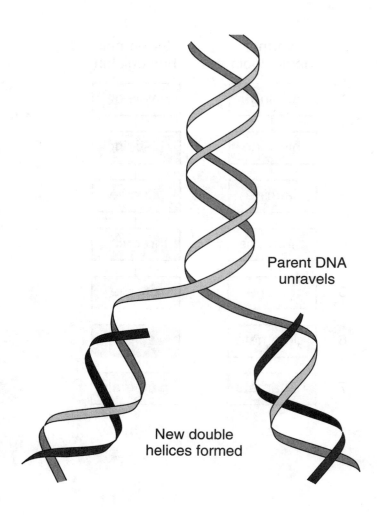

Parent DNA
unravels

New double
helices formed

**Criminalistics: An Introduction
to Forensic Science, 7/E
Saferstein**

T-51   Recombinant DNA (Figure 13-6)

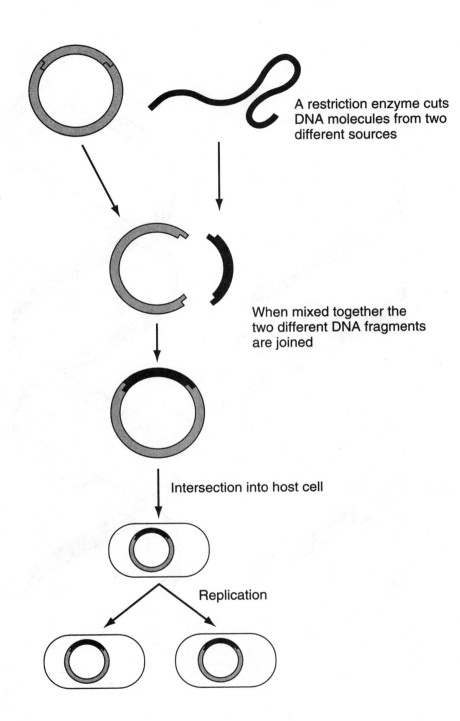

A restriction enzyme cuts
DNA molecules from two
different sources

When mixed together the
two different DNA fragments
are joined

Intersection into host cell

Replication

**Criminalistics: An Introduction
to Forensic Science, 7/E
Saferstein**

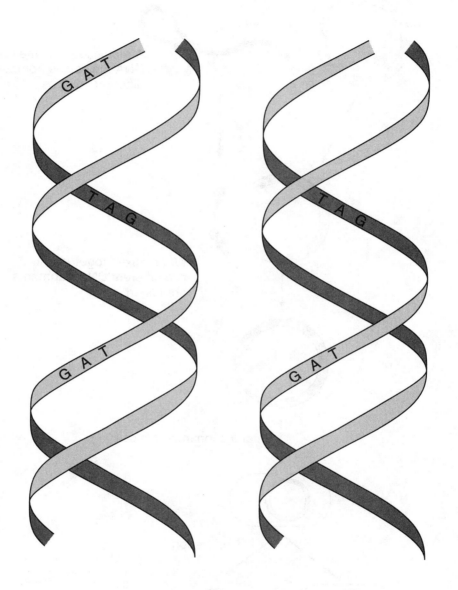

T-53 The DNA Typing Process (Figure 13-8)

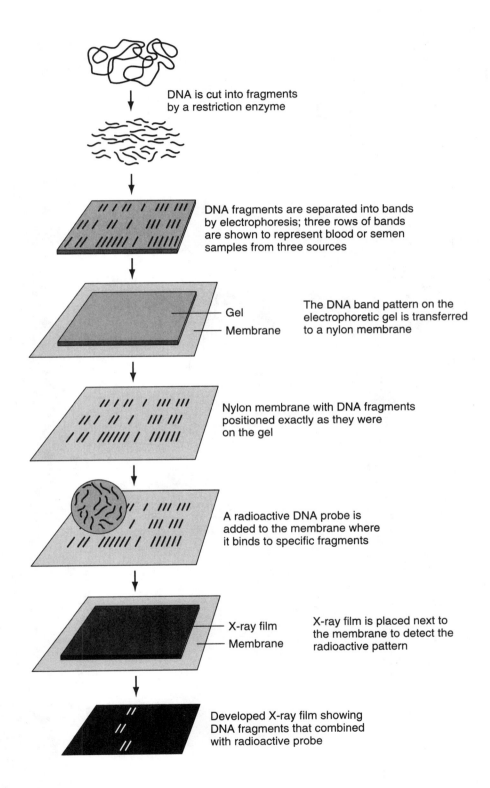

DNA is cut into fragments by a restriction enzyme

DNA fragments are separated into bands by electrophoresis; three rows of bands are shown to represent blood or semen samples from three sources

Gel
Membrane

The DNA band pattern on the electrophoretic gel is transferred to a nylon membrane

Nylon membrane with DNA fragments positioned exactly as they were on the gel

A radioactive DNA probe is added to the membrane where it binds to specific fragments

X-ray film
Membrane

X-ray film is placed next to the membrane to detect the radioactive pattern

Developed X-ray film showing DNA fragments that combined with radioactive probe

Criminalistics: An Introduction
to Forensic Science, 7/E
Saferstein

T-54 PCR Process for DNA Typing (Figure 13-11)

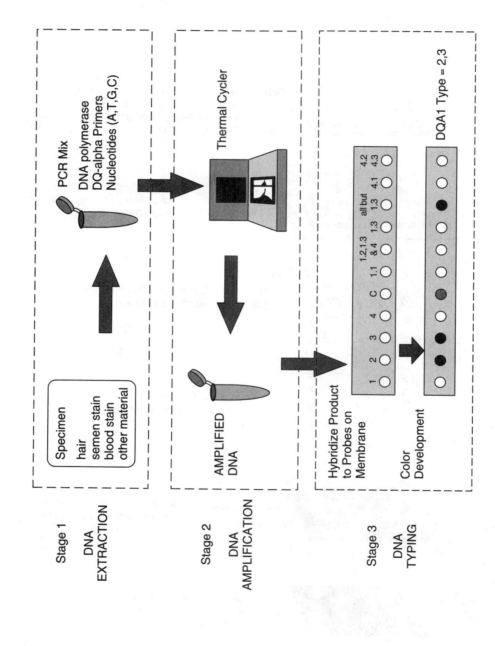

Criminalistics: An Introduction
to Forensic Science, 7/E
Saferstein

T-55   THO1 Variants (Figure 13-12)

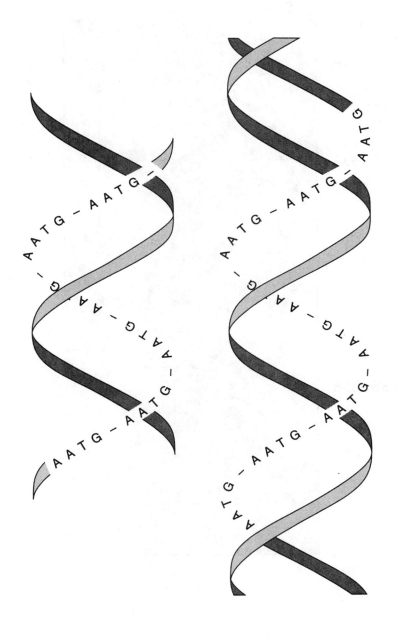

Criminalistics: An Introduction
to Forensic Science, 7/E
Saferstein

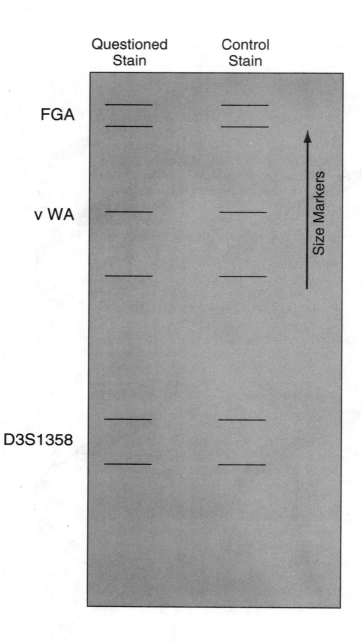

Criminalistics: An Introduction
to Forensic Science, 7/E
Saferstein

T-57 Separation of DNA Segments by Capillary Electrophoresis (Figure 13-14)

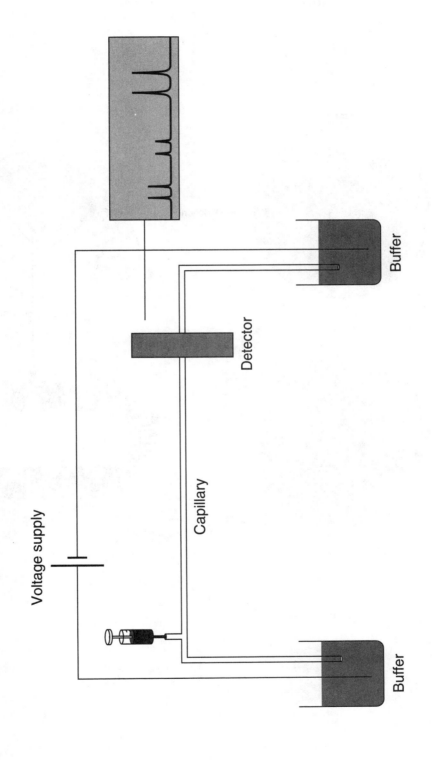

Voltage supply

Capillary

Detector

Buffer

Buffer

Criminalistics: An Introduction
to Forensic Science, 7/E
Saferstein

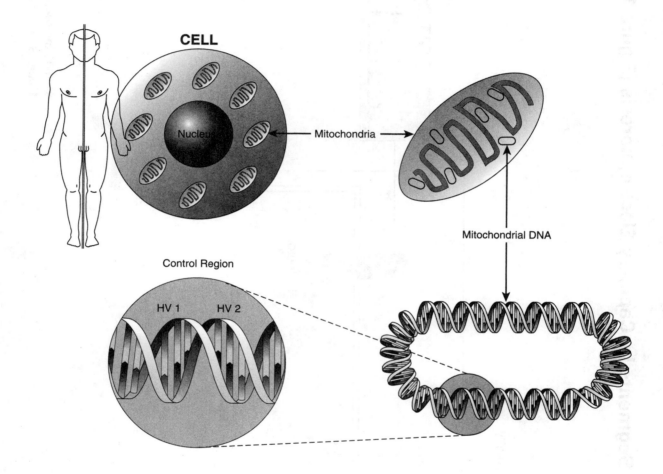

CELL

Nucleus

Mitochondria

Mitochondrial DNA

Control Region

HV 1   HV 2

**Criminalistics: An Introduction
to Forensic Science, 7/E
Saferstein**

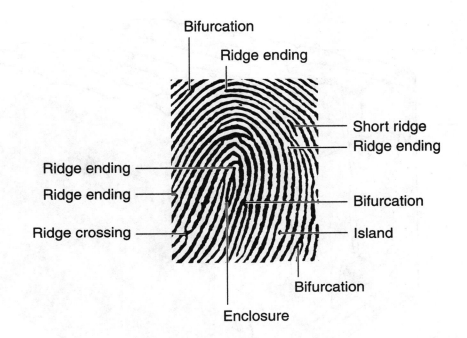

Bifurcation

Ridge ending

Short ridge

Ridge ending

Ridge ending

Ridge ending

Bifurcation

Ridge crossing

Island

Bifurcation

Enclosure

**Criminalistics: An Introduction
to Forensic Science, 7/E
Saferstein**

© **2001 by Prentice-Hall, Inc.
Upper Saddle River, New Jersey 07458**

Ridge island

Sweat pores

Epidermis

Papillae

Dermis

Duct of sweat gland

Sweat gland

Nerves of touch

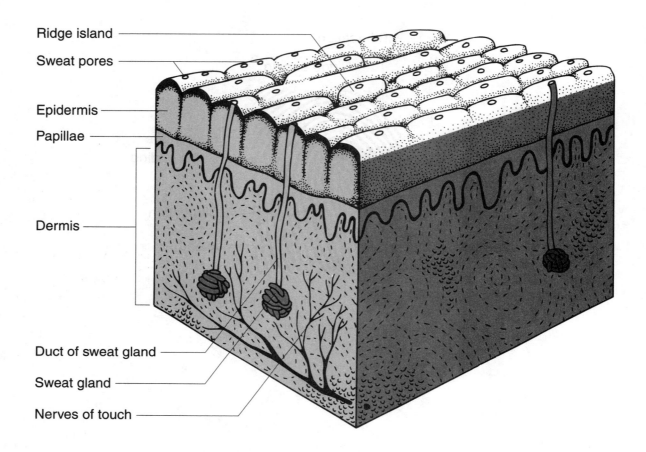

Criminalistics: An Introduction to Forensic Science, 7/E Saferstein

Core

Type line

Delta

Type line

**Criminalistics: An Introduction
to Forensic Science, 7/E
Saferstein**

T-62   Whorl Patterns (Figure 14-6)

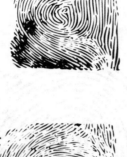

Plain whorl

Central pocket loop

Double loop

Accidental

Criminalistics: An Introduction
to Forensic Science, 7/E
Saferstein

© 2001 by Prentice-Hall, Inc.
Upper Saddle River, New Jersey 07458

T-63 Arch Patterns (Figure 14-7)

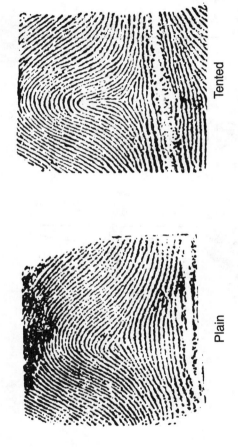

Plain

Tented

**Criminalistics: An Introduction
to Forensic Science, 7/E**
Saferstein

Latent Fingerprint Detection with the Aid of a Laser (Figure 14-11)

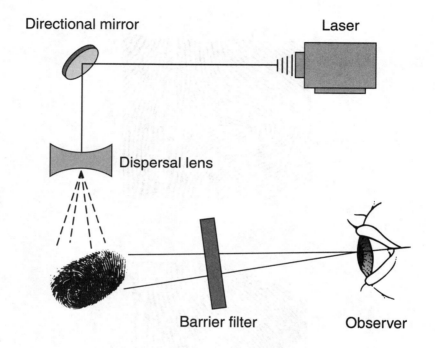

Criminalistics: An Introduction to Forensic Science, 7/E Saferstein

T-65   Internal View of a Gun Barrel (Figure 15-1)

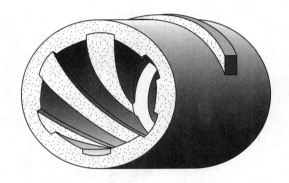

**Criminalistics: An Introduction
to Forensic Science, 7/E
Saferstein**

T-66 Parts of the IBIS System (Figure 15-10)

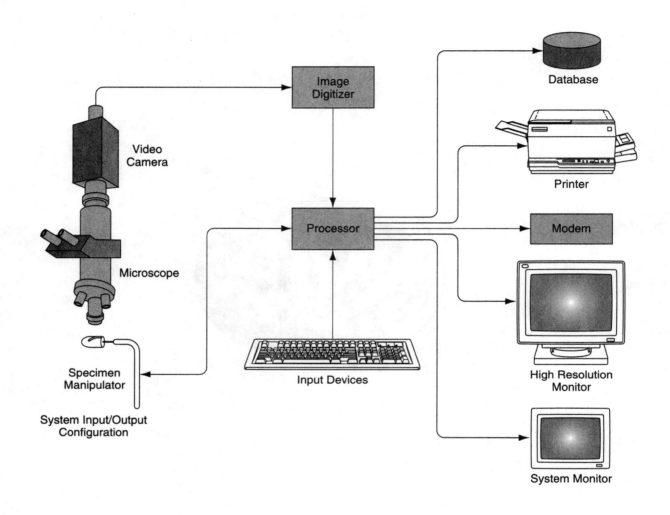

Video Camera

Image Digitizer

Database

Microscope

Processor

Printer

Modem

Specimen Manipulator

Input Devices

High Resolution Monitor

System Input/Output Configuration

System Monitor

**Criminalistics: An Introduction to Forensic Science, 7/E
Saferstein**

**© 2001 by Prentice-Hall, Inc.
Upper Saddle River, New Jersey 07458**

T-67 The Compound Microscope (Figure 4-1)

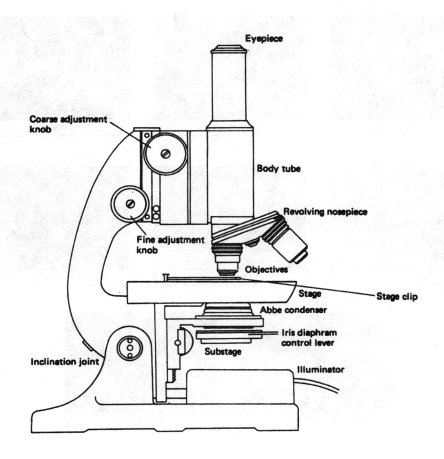

Eyepiece

Coarse adjustment knob

Body tube

Revolving nosepiece

Fine adjustment knob

Objectives

Stage

Stage clip

Abbe condenser

Iris diaphram control lever

Inclination joint

Substage

Illuminator

**Criminalistics: An Introduction
to Forensic Science, 7/E
Saferstein**

**© 2001 by Prentice-Hall, Inc.
Upper Saddle River, New Jersey 07458**

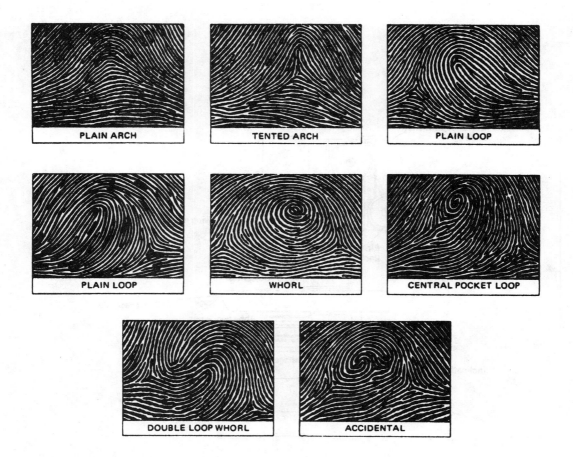

PLAIN ARCH   TENTED ARCH   PLAIN LOOP

PLAIN LOOP   WHORL   CENTRAL POCKET LOOP

DOUBLE LOOP WHORL   ACCIDENTAL

Criminalistics: An Introduction to Forensic Science, 7/E Saferstein

© 2001 by Prentice-Hall, Inc. Upper Saddle River, New Jersey 07458

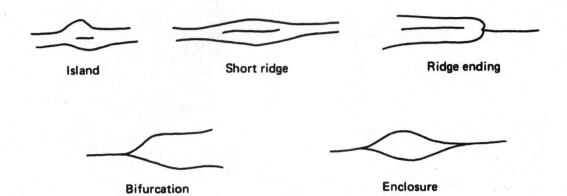

Island   Short ridge   Ridge ending

Bifurcation   Enclosure

**Criminalistics: An Introduction
to Forensic Science, 7/E
Saferstein**

Spinous

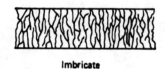

Coronal

Imbricate